FURNITURE FINISHING

NEW & REVISED

FURNITURE
FINISHING
NEW & REVISED

By Albert Brace Patton
& Clarence Lee Vaughn

DRAKE PUBLISHERS INC.
NEW YORK · LONDON

1-97

#1960549

Published in 1976 by
Drake Publishers, Inc.
801 Second Avenue
New York, N.Y. 10017

Library of Congress Cataloging in Publication Data

Pattou, Albert Brace.
     Furniture; furniture finishing, decoration and pataching.
     A new and complete work on furniture of all kinds, with
     full practical instruction on finishing, patching and decora-
     tion—materials, tools and processes, by Albert Brace Pattou
     and Clarence Lee Vaughn. New York, Drake Publishers 1971
     1970.
               551 p. illus. 21cm.

     1. Furniture finishing. I. Vaughn, Clarence Lee, 1890—   joint
     author. II. Title.
     TS885.P38   1971   684.1'0443   73-24061
                                                                  MARC
     Library of Congress   71[2]

Printed in The United States of America

CONTENTS

PREFACE

In a work of so broad a scope, the authors wish us to say, first of all, that no attempt has been made to exhaust the subject—such a task would require at least ten volumes the size of this one. In the matter of processes of finishing, patching and decorating furniture, there are many different minds and different practices, and not all by any means are agreed as to the best ideas and the best methods of executing them. The chief aim, therefore, has been in all cases to give up-to-date and proved practical instruction as to materials and processes.

For many years the publishers, with their extensive patronage for their books along the line of painting, decorating, home furnishing and wood finishing, have had almost countless requests for a book of this kind. The great difficulty has been to find anyone with the knowledge and practical experience who could and would write it. We feel highly elated therefore, in our successful efforts in inducing Messrs. Pattou and Vaughn to undertake the work. Their training and experience have been such that, we believe the results of their work are entitled to the confidence of all who are interested in this subject.

Mr. Albert Brace Pattou, of the Adams and Elting Co., Chicago, has written extensively for the past 16 years on furniture finishing methods, the articles appearing in various trade journals. Mr. Clarence Lee Vaughn, of Chicago, has been interested for twenty years in the manufacture and distribution of furniture finishing and patching materials. For several years he has been conducting in Chicago a school of furniture finishing and patching, and is therefore familiar not only with the materials, but with practical methods of applying them.

ACKNOWLEDGMENTS

We take this opportunity to express the indebtedness of both the authors and publishers to the following individuals and concerns who have aided in the production of this work.

First of all, to Mr. F. N. Vanderwalker for the use of several excellent illustrations from his highly successful books on Painting, Wood Finishing, Wall Decoration, Stencils, etc.

To *The American Painter and Decorator*, of St. Louis, for permission to reprint parts of articles by Mr. Pattou, which have appeared in that excellent journal in past years.

To the Metropolitan Museum of Art, New York, and The Art Institute, Chicago, for the illustrations shown in Book I, also:

The DeVilbiss Company, Toledo, Ohio
Gerts Lumbard & Co., Chicago
Mitchell & Mitchell, Ft. Smith, Ark.
Empire Case Goods Co., Jamestown, N. Y.
Behnke-Fink Co., Chicago
S. Karpen Bros., Chicago
Bemis Mfg. Co., Sheboygan Falls, Wis.
Union Furniture Co., Jamestown, N. Y.
Ypsilanti Reed Furniture Co., Ypsilanti, Mich.
Kernes Mfg. Co., Chicago
General Fireproofing Co., Youngstown, Ohio
Richardson Bros., Sheboygan Falls, Wis.
Northern Furniture Co., Sheboygan, Wis.
Au Cri Modern, New York
American Emblem Co., Utica, N. Y.
The Lane Co., Alta Vista, Va.
Standard Screen Co., Chicago
Unagusta Mfg. Co., Hazelwood, N. C.
Peabody Seating Co., No. Manchester, Ind.
Cable Nelson Piano Co., South Haven, Mich.
Hedrick-Blessing Studio, Chicago
D .H. Fritts & Co., Chicago
Dover Mfg .Co., New York
Hansen Furniture Co.. Chicago
Standard Chair Co., Thomasville, N. C.
Coons Mfg. Co., Abingdon, Ill.

Troy Sunshade Co., Troy, Ohio
Hastings Table Co., Hastings, Mich.
Crane & McMahon Inc., St. Marys, Ohio
Bay View Furniture Co., Holland, Mich.
Romweber Co., Batesville, Ind.
Paasche Air Brush Co., Chicago
White Furniture Co., Mebane, N. C.
Wiener & Co., Milwaukee, Wis.
Bink's Manufacturing Co., Chicago
Lullabye Furniture Co., Stevens Point, Wis.
American Woodcraft Corp., Evansville, Ind.
American Walnut Manufacturers Association, Chicago
Saginaw Furniture Shops, Saginaw, Mich., and Chicago
Glidden Co., Cleveland, Ohio
Storkline Furniture Corp., Chicago
Mersman Bros., Celina, Ohio
Grand Rapids Chair Co., Grand Rapids, Mich.
Flexo Products Corp., Chicago
Royal Metal Mfg. Co., Chicago
Imperial Furniture Co., Grand Rapids, Mich.
Golden Star Polish Mfg. Co., Kansas City, Mo.
Crosley Radio Corp., Cincinnati, Ohio
Philco Radio & Television Corp, Philadelphia, Pa.

CHAPTER I

BRIEF HISTORY OF FURNITURE FINISHING

ANY account of furniture finishing and finishing materials must necessarily be brief, owing to the limited supply of information on the subject. In the book of Jeremiah we find, "Woe unto him who sayeth: I will build me a wide house, sealed with cedar and lined with vermillion." This is the first historical mention of a paint material. Painted furniture in the tomb of King Tutankhamen gave evidence of the art of painting over three thousand years ago. We have evidence of paint being used four thousand years before Christ.

Sculpture was first highly developed by the Greeks, and painting was not fully developed until the Italian Renaissance of the fifteenth century. Paint pigments (mineral and earth colors), organic dyes, and white lead were first mentioned by Theophrastus about 350 B. C. White lead was known as "cerrussa" and found in Europe in small quantities as carbonate of lead. This material was mentioned also by Pliny, about 50 A. D.

The original Dutch process of making white lead is about 300 years old and attributed to Stratingh. The process was patented in England in 1622. Leclaire discovered the use of zinc white used in paint, in 1845. Lampblack was used two thousand years ago by the Chinese and was obtained by burning oil in lamps with little air and collecting soot on the chimneys. Lampblack found on Egyptian mummy cases was found on the shores of the Black Sea.

Dr. Wm. Henry Perkin of England discovered aniline in 1856 and it was later developed by chemists in Germany and America. The earliest blue indigo was used in Egypt and India and mentioned by the early Byzantine writers. Natural ultramarine blue was used centuries ago, but the artificial product was developed

1

by Christian Gmelin in France, 1828. Prussian blue was discovered by Diesbach in Berlin in 1710.

Ochre, the earliest yellow pigment, was used by the Egyptians, but chrome yellow was made but a hundred years ago. Malachite and verdigris were the first green pigments used and have been found on the wall paintings of Pompeii. Chrome green, so common today, was first made in France in 1838.

Waxes were first used as vehicles for colored paints which were later mixed with animal fats and oils to lower the melting point of the wax. For interiors, fish glue, vegetable gum and white of egg were the earliest mediums used for mixing with colors.

Use of oil.—The first mention of a drying oil as a paint vehicle was by Actius, a Greek physician of the sixth century, and this may have been linseed oil. In the library of Lucca is a manuscript giving information on how to make a transparent varnish from amber gum and linseed oil. One who understands the make-up of varnishes of today can see that the fundamental operations in making varnish have not changed materially, although new and more refined equipment, methods and raw materials have been developed.

Oil painting was developed in the eleventh century, but was a very crude art, for it was not until the sixteenth century that oil painting was fully developed. The development of the paint industry was slow until the revival of industry after the Civil War, which brought on many improvements in every line of industry.

Turpentine.—About three hundred years ago turpentine was discovered in the Southern American colonies by early settlers. Kauri gum was brought into England in 1769, following Captain Cook's discovery of New Zealand, and this is a very important gum in the manufacture of high-grade varnishes. China wood oil, or tung oil, used by the Chinese centuries ago in all kinds of lacquering, was introduced into spar or waterproof varnishes about thirty years ago.

A gradual development in the paint and varnish industry, rather than a radical change, is the result after nine centuries of improvement. One could easily say that the furniture industry has been far behind other industries, especially the finishing of furniture. It is not so long ago that material was put on furniture with a trowel while hot, before the use of brushes, and the varnish maker of colonial days peddled his varnish about the streets.

Formerly all material was applied by hand, with what is known as a sponge or rubber, over the entire surface of the furniture. This method necessarily took several weeks to finish a large piece of furniture, and as a result, only kings and nobles were in a position to have fine furniture, and even then, had to wait weeks for completion of a single piece.

After the advent of brushes the application of varnish and paint became much easier and faster. Paint and varnish materials in the last few years have been applied mostly by the air-gun or spray. This method of application of materials is the best method of applying thin liquids, because no brush marks or laps can be seen after coating. Stain, shellac, enamels, varnishes and lacquers may all be applied by this method.

LACQUER MATERIALS

The advent of nitro-cellulose lacquers into furniture finishing is a very recent experiment. It has passed the experimental stage, as far as being accepted, for many of the manufacturers of cabinet furniture today are using some form of nitro-cellulose lacquer for a finish coating over water stain. This material was not at first adopted universally by furniture manufacturers because it was so radically different from varnish in drying, application and other properties, but time has ironed out these preliminary difficulties and proved its suitability for furniture use. With the use of clear lacquer it is advisable to choose carefully the type of stain and filler to avoid troubles. Water and "non-grain-raising" liquid stains have proven most satisfactory and paste wood fillers, for use under lacquer, are available.

Lacquer enamel, made from a combination of nitro-cellulose and pigments, mixed or ground together, forms a large part of the opaque materials used, instead of enamel formerly used for painting furniture. A good covering lacquer can be made by adding colors ground in japan with a suitable clear nitro-cellulose lacquer, although it is advisable to use ready-made lacquer enamels whenever they are available.

Clear lacquers were first made by using resin gums for solids but later the development of synthetic gums have improved the quality of lacquer films as to tenacity and toughness and we may expect greater advancement in the manufacture of all finish material as a result of the development of synthetic gums.

DECORATIVE MATERIALS

To furnish bright furniture for drab surroundings or to satisfy a taste for the unusual, many different decorative finishes have been developed. Gilded furniture is quite an old thing with the Italians and French, but has never been popular in America.

Before the advent of aniline stains, painted furniture, decorated in gold, was the vogue, but since permanent dyes were first used for stain, decorative furniture has been secondary in importance. In Book II will be found a description of all the modern decorative finishes and how to create them. By using different colors in polychrome finishing, many effects can be created. Glazing over different enamel ground coats and painting of floral and other designs is another type of decorative finish. Decalcomania transfers are now used in cheaper decorative furniture, rather than the high priced hand-painting, and many beautiful effects can be created at a low cost.

After all, plain wood finishing has followed the lines of least resistance and all woods are stained usually to imitate oak, walnut and mahogany. Few woods can imitate oak, but walnut and mahogany can be successfully imitated by skillful manipulation of stain. The above mentioned woods were the first to be made into furniture, especially the first two, and because of the naturally beautiful figure or grain of these woods, all others are made to look like them, with the possible exception of bird's-eye or curly maple.

In studying the advance in materials made for furniture finishing, one cannot help feeling that the real finishing material, or ideal one for the finish coat, is yet to be developed, one that will not scratch or mark or be affected by ordinary chemicals. This may be the next development, who knows?

CHAPTER II

FURNITURE WOODS

A TYPICAL piece of modern wood furniture is the creation of both science and art. Science gives it stability; art gives it beauty. For its purposes science gives preference to solid woods for structural parts, veneer and plywood for larger and flat surfaces. Art, on the other hand, achieves its purpose through design, decoration, color and finish.

SOLID WOODS

In this work our concern is not with the details of furniture construction, interesting and ingenious as they may be, but rather with the surfaces to be finished. As such, solid wood appears in two qualities. The first, and more expensive, constitutes such naturally beautiful woods as mahogany, walnut, maple and oak. Being strong, they are favored on finer pieces for posts, legs, stretchers, and rails. These same woods, with the exception of maple, are also extensively used, as well as a few others, for hand carving on reproductions of Gothic, Jacobean, Elizabethan, Italian Renaissance and some French originals. Maple is used for whole pieces in the entire construction of much Early American furniture.

In production furniture, other solid woods such as birch, red and sap gum, tupelo, black gum and magnolia are widely employed as frames and legs, and sometimes for the whole piece, first, because they are less costly and secondly, because having unobtrusive markings and being in the majority almost white, they may be stained to imitate, or at least harmonize with the more expensive hardwoods mentioned.

Birch, black gum and tupelo for example, may be stained to very closely approximate mahogany or maple; red and sap gum,

6

tupelo, magnolia and southern willow, in the same degree, to give the appearance of walnut. Pecan is another wood that is coming into occasional use in place of walnut, which, though lighter in color, it resembles. Unlike the other woods mentioned, which all have tiny pores, pecan requires a filler.

The darker the color of the finish, the more difficult it is to detect substitutes. Because of the difference in quality, it is now required by law to differentiate in advertising between, for example, (1) "walnut" or "mahogany" furniture, (2) "walnut and gum" or "mahogany and gum," and (3) "mahogany finish" or "walnut finish," the latter terms to designate furniture made entirely of some other wood.

VENEERS

Veneers are thin sheets of wood manufactured almost exclusively for use in making plywood, a product in which several plies or pieces of veneer are glued to each other or to a lumber core. The grain of any one ply is usually at right angles to the adjacent layers, in order to lend greater strength.

For the greater part of furniture construction, plywood has many advantages:

(1) Through balanced construction, it reduces the natural tendency of wood to shrink or swell with atmospheric changes, at the same time affording maximum strength together with minimum weight.

(2) It makes possible curved effects as on serpentine desk fronts or grand piano rims, and the rounded corners of Modern furniture.

(3) It combines the strength of sturdy, though unattractive woods, with the beauty of fine cabinetwoods.

(4) It offers to the general public at moderate prices many handsome woods, too rare or costly for solid construction.

(5) It affords opportunity for perfect matching, since veneers may be cut thin enough to insure almost identical patterns on consecutive sheets.

Present day plywood-constructed furniture is the result of years of patient scientific research; but veneered furniture dates back to Egypt and the days of the Roman Empire. Then, and for many centuries, however, it was reserved only for the rich and powerful. One of the most celebrated historical pieces is the "Cabinet du Roi," the elaborate desk designed by Riesener for Louis XV, which took nine years to complete, and cost over a million francs. Made of veneer and plywood throughout, it now stands in the Louvre Museum in Paris, over two hundred years later, as beautiful as the day the king received it.

A separate and interesting volume could be written concerning the romantic world-wide origins of the beautiful woods going to make up the wide choice of modern veneers. Our concern is rather with the cuttings and varieties most commonly employed in modern furniture making, and the style or period of the pieces in which they most commonly appear. The latter relationship is indicated in the list below:

Louis XV—Rosewood, mahogany, walnut, beech, inlays
Louis XVI—Beech, mahogany, walnut, rosewood, satinwood
Empire—Mahogany, ebony, rosewood
Jacobean—Oak, some walnut
William and Mary—Walnut
Queen Anne—Walnut
Chippendale—Mahogany
Hepplewhite—Mahogany, satinwood, rosewood, inlays
Sheraton—Satinwood, mahogany with rare woods for inlays
Adam Brothers—Mahogany, satinwood
Early American—Maple, pine, birch
Colonial—Mahogany, black walnut
Duncan Phyfe—Mahogany mainly
Contemporary Classic—Fruitwood, aspen, bleached walnut and mahogany, variety of light woods
Modern—Practically all furniture woods, used individually or in a variety of combinations.

CUTTINGS

All in all, some hundred or more species of veneers are now

used in the manufacture of furniture. From each of these different woods a variety of effects may be obtained, depending upon the method of cutting. Figure types and grain character in veneers are determined in four different ways (see illustrations) :

(1) By varying the direction in which the knife or saw passes through the wood. Example: Quartered and flat cut veneers may both be cut from the trunk of the tree, and yet show different figures.

(2) By selecting different sections of the tree, or cutting de-

Cherry backgammon board with matched inlaid birch.

formed or abnormal portions. Example: Longwood, stumpwood, crotch and burl all have characteristics peculiar to that section of the tree alone.

(3) By selecting those species in which the difference in color and density between spring wood and summer wood is distinct. Example: Stripes in quartered walnut are formed by growth rings.

Inlaid cherry and birch chess board.

(4) By cutting the wood in order to expose the rays, the end or curly grain. Example: Three major methods, each with its subdivisions, are used in cutting veneers: slicing, sawing, and rotary lathe. All give different results.

Matched cherry table top with inlaid cribbage board.

FANCY OR FACE VENEERS

Fancy or face veneers are those used on the exposed surfaces of plywood panels for furniture. They are selected for their color, figure, matching possibilities, grain, and general appearance. They may be carefully chosen domestic woods or rare, imported ones. A number in both groups are illustrated with this text.

MAHOGANY
KHAYA IVORENSIS
SWIETENIA MAHAGONI
SWIETENIA MACROPHYLLA

Africa, the West Indies, and the Americas, including Mexico, Central America and South America, supply the three species which make up all genuine mahogany. Each of these species varies somewhat in color and texture, and has its own particular characteristics. African Mahogany presents an amazing variety of figures, ranging from a straight stripe to a rich mottle or fiddleback. It is also noted for its enormous crotches and swirls. West Indian Mahogany is preferred for fine furni-

Honduras (American) Mahogany.

African Mahogany.

ture and carved work, because of its close grain and silky texture. The American Mahoganies have a rather straight grain and compact texture, and are generally used for solid parts.

Mahogany holds an enviable position among fine cabinetwoods. It is extensively used in both solid and veneer form for the various Georgian period reproductions, French Colonial adaptations and modern pieces. Chippendale, Hepplewhite, Adam Brothers, Sheraton and Duncan Phyfe are but a few of the old Masters who appreciated the fine qualities of this wood.

Improper finishing has probably done more damage to Mahogany than to any one other wood. For years a deep red stain was applied, completely obliterating its figure and character. Recently, however, as a result of the popularity of lighter woods, finishes are revealing, rather than concealing, the beauty of the wood.

At the present time Mahogany is generally finished with a light reddish-brown or brown stain, with or without filler, polished or dull-rubbed. Natural or bleached effects are not uncommon. (*See Book I, Chapter IV*) A natural finish, with no stain whatsoever, will give a light claret to deep golden-brown color to the wood. If filler is to be used, from 12 to 14 lbs. to the gallon is necessary for the larger-pored African Mahogany, slightly less for West Indian and American. Cuban Mahogany is particularly suitable for colonial and "Old World" finishes, since the wood itself has a dark reddish-brown color.

WALNUT
JUGLANS NIGRA
JUGLANS REGIA
JUGLANS CALIFORNICA

Through the ages walnut has played an important part in fine furniture construction. Although Circassian, French, English, Claro and American (Black) Walnut are all familiar names to the furniture trade, 90% to 95% of the Walnut used in the United States is of the last named species.

The color of American Walnut varies from a light creamy sapwood through the warm grays to a light brown. Pores are

American Walnut.

irregular in size, plainly visible and evenly distributed. Walnut veneers are noted for their wide range of figures, which include burl, crotch, stumpwood and plain stripe to highly figured

American Walnut.

longwood. Logs are sliced, quarter sliced, rotary cut or sawn, depending upon purpose and figure desired.

Walnut is used extensively for both solid and veneer work. It has the close, even grain necessary for carvings such as found on French and Early English furniture, the bending strength and shock-resisting ability important for legs, rails, posts and stretchers, and the warmth, beauty, stability, matching possibilities, and the excellent finishing qualities required of a good cabinetwood. These qualifications account for the popularity of Walnut for both modern and traditional furniture.

When finished natural (for which absolutely no stain is applied) a filler either darker or lighter than the wood is most effective. Although Walnut has a warm color all through the wood, it may be stained lightly before filling, if desired. For modern designs it is frequently bleached. (*See Book I, Chapter XI*) While usually given a dull-rubbed finish, this wood is susceptible to practically any treatment commonly used on other species, and may either be filled or left open-pored.

OAK
QUERCUS BOREALIS
QUERCUS ALBA
QUERCUS SESSILIFLORA

Oak used in the furniture trade comes principally from three types of trees, the domestic Red Oak and White Oak, and English Brown Oak. The Red and White Oak groups each consist of a number of closely allied species. Of the two, White Oak is of greater importance in furniture manufacture. It is found in the eastern half of the United States.

The pores of Oak are large, especially in the spring wood, decreasing abruptly in the summer wood. They vary somewhat according to species. In finishing, they may be filled, partially filled, or left open. Figured wood such as found in Walnut and Mahogany is rarely developed by Oak, but this wood does have a characteristic "figure" caused by the unusually prominent medullary rays. This shows up as a "flake" when the rays are cut lengthwise, or "hen-scratch" when cut crosswise.

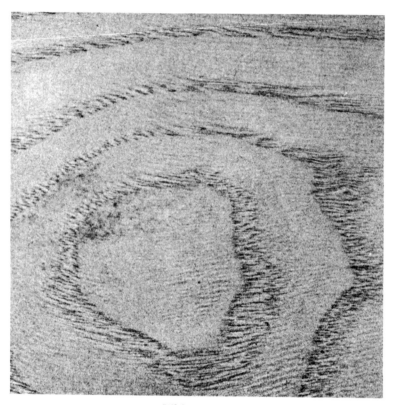

White Oak.

The majority of domestic oak, when used for furniture, goes into drawer bottoms, office desks, dinette sets, and Early English reproductions, with their massive carved work. Some Modern furniture is also made of this wood. Treatment of Oak varies somewhat, depending upon usage.

English Brown Oak.

MAPLE
ACER SACCHARUM

Maple ranks high among our important commercial timbers. Most of the supply used by the furniture industry comes from northern U. S. A. and Canada, and consists mainly of the sugar maple, known also as hard, or rock maple. This wood ranges from a light pink to a reddish brown color, with very tiny, regular pores, which require no filler.

Much Early American furniture is made of solid maple. Because of its strength and hardness, maple is also useful in solid form for legs, posts and rails of many suites, whether made entirely of this species, or of some harmonious wood.

Figured logs are selected for cutting into veneers, producing fiddleback, blister, curly and birds eye maple. These daintily figured veneers are popular as base and trim woods for bedroom and dining room suites, radios and other furniture.

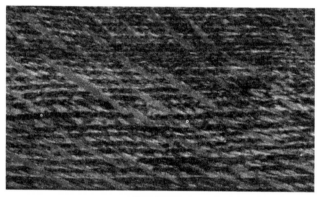

Red Oak.

Maple may be bleached for Modern (see Book I, Chapter XI) and to give the blonde maple effects, finished natural, or stained in various shades of amber, taffy, and honey color, or even silver grey, to imitate harewood. Glazes for antiquing are frequently applied over the stain. For bleached effects a white lacquer is used. The finish is usually dull-rubbed.

RED GUM
LIQUIDAMBAR STYRACIFLUA

Several species of Gum are used in the manufacture of furniture, but Red Gum is of most importance to the finisher. This timber grows in the southern central part of the United States.

Red Gum has very small pores, and a smooth surface. The heartwood, used for exposed parts, as well as for understructure, is a reddish brown. The sapwood has a grayish white color. Large quantities of this wood go into the manufacture of production furniture, sometimes for entire suites, although generally for smaller pieces such as occasional tables and chairs, and for legs, posts, stretchers and frames of suites made of some other wood. No filler is required, although sometimes used to give an even color, and the wood is usually stained to resemble walnut, or, in some cases, mahogany.

Red Gum.

ORIENTALWOOD
ENDIANDRA PALMERSTONI

Orientalwood, one of the newer woods, comes from the northern part of Queensland, in Australia. It is brown in color, with a salmon, green or grey cast, sometimes marked with black bandings. Figures available range from a plain stripe, particularly adaptable to diamond or V-matching, to a mottled fiddle back and roll. Almost all logs are cut on the quarter to emphasize the stripe. The pores of this wood are medium sized, visible to the eye, and fairly uniform in size and distribution. The grain is usually straight, but sometimes wavy.

Large quantities of Orientalwood go into the manufacture of bedroom and dining room suites, radios, pianos and other furniture. The wood is probably most pleasing with an amber stain, a light brown filler, and a polished surface.

Orientalwood.

PRIMA VERA
TABEBUIA DONNELL-SMITHII

Prima Vera is found throughout the coastal region of Mexico. southward to Nicaragua. This timber produces a pale yellow to light yellowish brown veneer, with a grain ranging from fairly straight to roey. Pores are visible, but not very distinct without lens.

Typical figures of Prima Vera are broken stripe, mottle and a fine feather grain. Logs are generally cut on the quarter and some crotches and swirls are used. Veneers are frequently employed as the major wood for modern bedroom and some dining room suites, as well as for certain types of period furniture.

Prima Vera is either filled and finished natural, bleached, or stained a light brown, or, in some cases, to imitate Satinwood. It is usually polished.

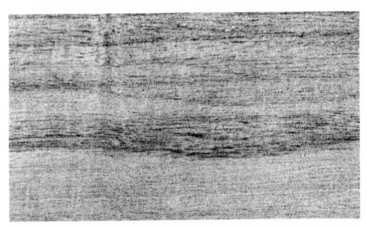

Prima Vera.

SATINWOOD
CHLOROXYLON SWIETENIA
AND
ZANTHOXYLUM FLAVUM

Satinwood is an old favorite. Sheraton, Hepplewhite and the Adam Brothers fully appreciated the value of this fine cabinet-wood, and no Louis XVI room is complete without a Satinwood piece of some kind.

Satinwood consists of two species, one (Chloroxylon swietenia) a native of Ceylon and southern India, the other (Zanthoxylum flavum) coming from the West Indies. The former, known as East Indian Satinwood, produces most of the veneers now on the United States market. Almost everyone is familiar with this silky-sheened, golden-yellow wood, that grows even more beautiful as it mellows with age. It is generally cut on the quarter, to take full advantage of the narrow parallel bandings. Veneers have a fine and even texture, and indistinct pores, filled with gummy inclusions that are light colored and do not show after the wood is finished. Only a small amount of filler, or none at all, is required.

Satinwood.

Present day usage of Satinwood includes period reproductions, inlays and bandings, and some modern furniture. This wood is either finished natural, or stained a light brown or orange yellow.

MYRTLE BURLS
UMBELLULARIA CALIFORNICA

The Myrtle tree is a native of California and Oregon. Only the burls are used in modern furniture construction. Often, however, they appear in a peculiar mixture of plainwood, stumpwood and burl figure, which is known as "cluster."

The pores of this wood are numerous and fairly regular in

distribution. Finish brings out the highlights, and makes the veneer even more attractive in appearance. A natural finish is generally used, although occasionally the wood is bleached. A light brown filler, and either dull or polished sheen is appropriate.

Myrtle burls are found particularly in modern furniture, where they are employed on large surfaces. The "clusters" are prized for their extraordinary matching possibilities.

Japanese Ash (Tamo).

OTHER POPULAR CABINET WOODS

Illustrations of some of the more frequently used cabinet-woods will be found on subsequent pages.

ASH, JAPANESE (TAMO) :—*Source:* Japan and Korea. *Pores:* Open and numerous in Spring growth; very small in Summer-wood. *Color Range:* White to light brown. *Finish:* May be filled or left open-pored; natural, or stained amber; polished, dull, or soft-waxed.

ASPEN:—*Source:* Eastern Coast U. S. A. *Pores:* Tiny. *Color Range:* Light straw. *Finish:* Usually finished natural or in an amber color, with a dull-rubbed or polished surface.

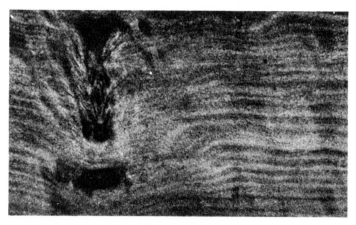

Aspen Wood.

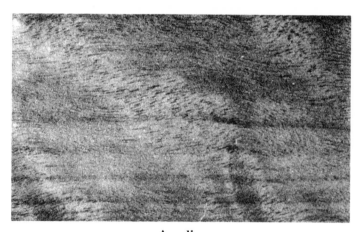

Avodire.

AVODIRE:—*Source:* West Africa. *Pores:* Rather small, visible, but not distinct, due to lack of colored deposits. Numerous, but not crowded. *Color Range:* Lustrous creamy white to pale yellow. *Finish:* Small amount of filler, or none at all; natural, or stained light brown or golden yellow; dull-rubbed or polished surface; finished like Satinwood.

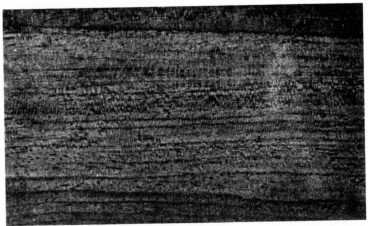

Bubinga.

BIRCH: — *Source:* U. S. A. and Canada. *Pores:* Small. *Color:* White to red-brown. *Finish:* May be finished natural, as in Curly Birch veneers, or stained to imitate Mahogany, and sometimes Walnut, especially when used for solid parts.

BUBINGA:—*Source:* West Africa. *Pores:* Small, not very numerous, irregularly spaced. *Color Range:* Pale to deep flesh red, with darker thin stripes. *Finish:* Requires filler, which should harmonize with stain; finished natural or like Mahogany; dull-rubbed or polished.

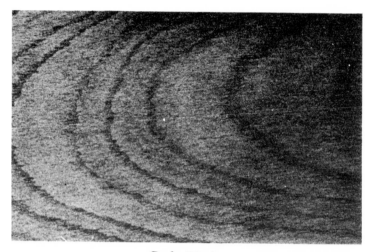

Curly Birch.

Narra.

NARRA:—*Source:* Philippines. *Pores:* Large. *Color Range:* Pale yellow, to salmon, to deep red. *Finish:* Requires considerable filler; finished natural, or to imitate Satinwood; polished or dull-rubbed.

Paldao.

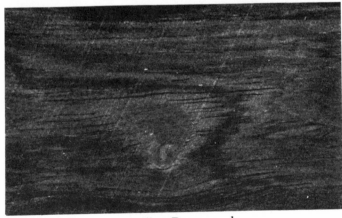

Brazilian Rosewood.

PALDAO:—*Source:* Philippines. *Pores:* Moderate size, distinctly visible; fairly numerous, rather uniformly distributed. *Color Range:* Variable from greenish grey to medium brown, with distinct chocolate brown or black streaks. *Finish:* Usually filled with walnut-colored filler, and finished natural, with polished surface. May be very lightly stained.

ROSEWOOD, BRAZILIAN:—*Source:* South America. *Pores:* Variable in size; mostly rather large and distinct; not very numer-

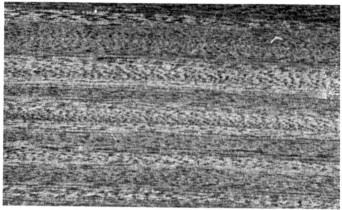

Sapeli.

ous; irregularly distributed. *Color Range:* Red to brown, streaked with black lines. *Finish:* Oil in pores makes careful finishing necessary, or surface may check. Usually filled with light red Mahogany filler, and given a polished finish; may be stained, but natural preferred.

SAPELI:—*Source:* Africa. *Pores:* Rather large and irregular. *Color Range:* Medium to dark brown, with pronounced stripe. *Finish:* Can be stained to imitate Mahogany, or simply filled with light brown Mahogany filler, and given a dull-rubbed or polished finish.

Tigerwood.

TIGERWOOD:—*Source:* Africa. *Pores:* Numerous; visible; uniform in size and distribution. *Color Range:* Golden brown, with dark brown or black bands, producing striped effect. *Finish:* May be finished natural, or with amber stain; requires filler.

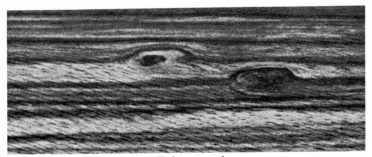

Zebrawood.

ZEBRAWOOD:—*Source:* Africa. *Pores:* Small, but distinct. *Color Range:* Yellow brown, with dark brown parallel stripes. *Finish:* Natural filler best; requires no staining; dull-rubbed or polished finish.

CHAPTER III

THE FINISHING ROOM, EQUIPMENT, MATERIALS, COLORS

THE first thing to be considered in the construction of a finishing room is light. Nothing is more necessary to insure perfect matching of colors, and avoidance of strain on the finishers' eyes. Furthermore many skips and rubbed-through places can be attributed to poor lighting facilities. If possible, there should be light on three sides of the finishing room, and the more wall space given to windows, the better.

If artificial lighting is necessary, and it is on dark days, the room should be so flooded with light, indirect if possible, that few shadows can be noticed. If the ceiling is painted a luminus white, an indirect light will not injure the eyes even though very strong. Lights should never be hung low near the workman, as the rest of the room will appear dark and many shadows will cause poor finishing.

Heat is another requisite and the room should never fall below 75° F. while work is progressing. The heat should be evenly distributed in the room. If the exhaust equipment is on opposite side of the room, all heating should be on the side fresh air is taken in. Of course the heat of the drying room should be raised to 100 degrees or more for quick oxidization of varnish coatings or enamels. Most production factories using varnish are equipped with drying systems designed to hasten the drying of the material. If lacquer or shellac is the finishing coat, it will not be necessary to have extra heat or a special drying system. With these materials coated pieces can be placed in the drying room with just comfortable room temperature, for they dry quickly.

An important thing to consider in any finishing room or drying room is the air-tight construction, so that no dust can be carried into the room from the outside to settle on finished work and thus cause pimples and more labor to rub out. Windows should be metal frame and tightly cased. Small openings may be allowed with double screening for ventilation. An efficient ventilating system should be installed, especially in large plants.

All partitions should be built of tile or plaster board with a painted surface that can be cleaned at intervals. Tongue and groove partitions cannot be relied upon for air-tight compart-

Home spraying operation in dust free area.

ments. Doors should be well built and be shut tight to exclude dust from other parts of the establishment.

The size of the finishing room depends entirely on the space required to handle the output of the cabinet room without crowding. Sometimes an entire floor, or even more, is given over to finishing alone. This can be done easily where the work is all finished in lacquer, but in case of varnish finishing, the room should be divided up into several rooms of different sizes and designated according to use as staining room, sanding room, filling room, flowing room, and drying room.

Cabinets should be constructed in the finishing room to hold materials to avoid waste and loss. Brushes are expensive and should be kept in a container for this purpose in the finishing

A"brush-keep"will keep brushes clean and in good condition.

room cabinet and in a "brush-keep," which can be easily made from japan dryer and thin shellac, or thin varnish. The finishing room and all cabinets should be fireproof. The same should hold for partitions and doors. Metal waste cans with tight covers should be provided for disposal of waste material.

SPRAYING EQUIPMENT

This equipment is made up of different parts made by different factories and assembled into a complete equipment. One concern will make a specialty of manufacturing the spray gun, another the compressor tank, another the motor, another the

Spray gun with one-finger trigger.

air storage tank, another the air scrubber, etc. Of course there. are several manufacturers making each of these parts of the equipment and there are various styles to choose from. This field is rapidly undergoing changes and one should secure literature from the different manufacturers of this equipment if contemplating a purchase. Full directions for operation is furnished the purchaser and service is given by most of the gun manufacturers.

The air scrubber, or oil and water extractor, as it is commonly called, is an absolute necessity in spraying lacquers or shellac. A very little oil in the lacquer will prevent quick drying and sometimes cause a great deal of trouble. Water of course will cause blushing, or a white film in the lacquer or shellac. A very cheap but effective scrubber can be made by cutting a piece of pipe three feet long and four inches in diameter, cutting threads

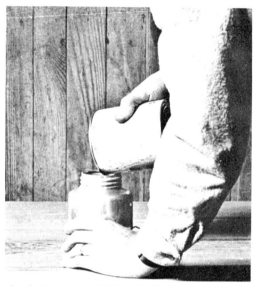

Stain is poured directly into spray tank.

on each end and capping. A tap should be made in the center of each end for the air hose connection, or the bottom tap can be on the side near the end and a tap in the bottom for a pet-cock to drain off the air and moisture. A fine mesh screen should be placed at the top, about one inch away, to prevent packing from clogging up the air line. The packing can be fine wood wool or excelsior lightly pressed into the pipe before placing the bottom cap. The scrubber should be placed upright between the air compressor and the gun, preferably near the spray booth. Whenever there is considerable collection of moisture at the pet-cock the cap should be removed and the excelsior changed for new, clean, dry stock.

The spray booth is a necessity where lacquer materials are used, for the odor must be carried off by a fan for the health and comfort of the workman. For ordinary furniture work a

Popular home spraying outfit.

booth just large enough to hold the largest piece of furniture is all that is necessary. Elevating turn tables are very handy and save time in turning the furniture when spraying.

RUBBING EQUIPMENT

Various kinds of rubbing machines are on the market. From a small portable machine with oscillating pads attached to one or two shoes, they are made in sizes up to a large machine that will rub surfaces as long as a bedrail or even longer. Factories use large rubbing machines for heavy duty and small machines operated by electricity and compressed air. One popular type of rubbing machine is equipped with two shoes to hold felt pads, about four inches square. These pads can be removed and sand· paper or steel wool pads attached. These machines are made with long and short stroke.

Electric sander.

FINISHING MATERIALS

The first thing to consider is the use of stains and what kind of stains should be used in the finishing room. Aniline stains are extensively used, and are the least expensive in most cases. Under this heading we have three different kinds of aniline stains, known as water, spirit, and oil stains. Water stain is by far the most desirable and the most permanent, being non-fading as a rule. Non-grain-raising liquid stains that will not raise the grain of the wood are permanent, quicker in drying, and non-bleeding. They are very popular under lacquers.

Electric "belt" sander.

Water brown, red and black are the most important under this heading. Occasionally one requires yellow or blue. Green, of course, can be made from yellow and blue, but some prefer to use malachite green.

To test a water stain for mixtures or adulterations, wet a piece of filter paper and blow from the hand a small amount of the powder over the paper. You can readily perceive whether the brown, for example, has any yellow or orange in it, or whether a red may have some black in it to make it appear deeper. Water stains should be dissolved by pouring water over them, heated to at least 180 degrees.

OIL STAINS

Oil stains are usually sold in liquid form and form a large part of the stains used by factories. They are easy to apply and can be bought in standard colors, but few are light-proof, and therefore should not be used on good furniture. Some oil aniline has recently been brought out that is supposed to be light-proof, and of course would be of great advantage on lower priced furniture on account of their easy application. These stains cannot be used under lacquer successfully on account of bleeding through. A good oil stain can be made from the dry powder, dissolved in solvent naphtha.

SPIRIT STAINS

These stains are usually sold in powder form for patching and should be kept in stock in the following colors: oak, fumed and golden, brown and red mahogany, American and French walnut, nigrosine, and auramine yellow.

SHADING STAINS

Shading stains are made from spirit aniline dissolved in alcohol with a small amount of shellac added for adherence.

Lacquer shading stains are made by the reduction of lacquer enamels, and by addition of lacquer reducer.

FILLERS

Chapter V on *Fillers* gives all the explanation necessary to the proper use of fillers. Any explanation of the manufacture of fillers is useless for the reason that no satisfactory test for them has been devised without a laboratory test. The best test is to try the filler under the material to be used. If it dries hard and fills properly, and if the material you apply over it does not disturb the color or soften it permanently it is correct. Good linseed oil fillers, ground in permanent earth colors, can be used anywhere.

FIRST COAT MATERIALS

Shellac is the most universally used of all firstcoaters and has the proper qualities of drying very hard and sealing the pores of close-grained woods. Orange shellac is bleached for what is known as "bone-dry" and cut with alcohol for white shellac varnish. Refined shellac is made from best vso and cut with alcohol for what we know as French varnish, used in patching. The wax content of the gum, similar to the comb in honey, is of course found in both orange and white shellac. Other grades of shellac, known as garnet (real dark red) and button lac (a clear red), are used in other industries and sometimes in the manufacture of stick shellac for filling holes in the finish.

A test for shellac as to cut and for purity is given below, although it is seldom one finds impurities in shellac today owing to the Federal Trade Commission ruling that all shellac should be labeled "Pure Shellac," provided no adulteration is used, and "Compound Shellac," if other gums were mixed with the shellac when cutting. There is as much need for some rule regarding the cut of shellac as for testing for impurities. The purchaser as a rule has no adequate means of testing shellac for the number of pounds of gum per gallon of alcohol.

In testing shellac the finisher usually takes into account the different qualities that make shellac an ideal firstcoater or a coating for the finishing operation. Easy tests can be made by anyone to determine adulteration or the number of pounds per gallon of alcohol. Two or three such tests are given below.

TEST SHELLAC FOR ADULTERATION

The U. S. Bureau of Standards gives the following test for non-volatile matter. The process is simple, but must be done accurately. Use two small friction can lids from a pint or quart can, clean perfectly and dry in an oven. Prepare two vials (common drug store variety) with tight corks. After agitating the shellac sample, pour a like amount in each vial by weight and weigh. Now weigh accurately each of the tin lids and then pour about thirty grams of the shellac from each vial into each lid. The determination is made in duplicate to avoid error. The following tabulation will suffice to show how the test is made :

Weight of bottle before pouring out sample   45.45 grams
Weight of bottle after sampling   42.75
Weight of liquid shellac in dish   2.70

The dishes containing the shellac are placed in an oven of 212 degrees and left for two hours or more, at which time all the volatile matter will have evaporated.

Weight of dish or lid plus non-volatile matter   20.42 grams
Original weight of dish   19.39
Weight of non-volatile matter in dish   1.03

Applying equation, $\frac{1.03}{2.70} = .381$, or 38.1% of non-volatile matter or gum. Hence the shellac varnish contained 62% alcohol and 38% shellac gum if pure.

Determining the Shellac Cut.—After finding the percentage of gum in the varnish, let y equal the percentage of non-volatile matter and x the cut, and with the equation below, figure the cut from any shellac sample.

$x = \dfrac{6.8y}{100y}$, substituting we have $x = \dfrac{6.8 \times 38.0}{100-38.0} = 4.17$ lbs. per gallon.

The following table given by the American Society for Testing Materials will give excellent help in determining the cut of shellac by weighing and comparing it with this table. This table shows the relation between orange and white shellac in cut and weight.

Cut in pounds per gallon.	Weight in pounds per gallon.	
	Orange	White
3.0	7.50	7.55
3.5	7.60	7.64
4.0	7.69	7.74
4.5	7.77	7.79
5.0	7.83	7.89
5.5	7.92	7.95
6.0	7.97	8.00

The slight discrepancy is the result of insoluble material taken out of orange shellac when cutting and the fact that from two to five per cent moisture is excluded by heating the shellac to 212° F.

Test for Gum Adulteration.—Coat a panel with orange or white shellac of any desired sample on one side and with a known quality sample on the other; place the panel in a jar containing turpentine or solvent naphtha and allow to stand for a few days. If the coat becomes tacky or soft, the varnish contains adulteration of gums commonly used in oil varnish. If the shellac varnish contains brittle gums, the results will be manifested by chipping off a varnish coat over the shellac by alternate heat and cold changes. Coat a panel on one side with a known pure sample of shellac; on the other side coat with the sample you wish to test. Allow usual time for drying, sand, and coat with a rubbing varnish of good quality. After this varnish is hard, place it in an oven for thirty minutes and then place in a refrigerator, or if in winter, place outside for a few hours. Repeat this several times and if impure, the undercoat will break away separating the bond between it and the varnish coat. It can be noticed by light grey patches under the varnish.

RUBBING VARNISHES

About the only tests of any value that can be made by the finisher on rubbing varnish, will be actual test panels submitted to the test likely to be encountered by the furniture in use. The extensive use of wood lacquers has induced experiment with synthetic gums in varnishes and developed varnishes of quick drying qualities with a very tough film.

Varnish intended for use on dining room furniture must of course be a tung oil varnish, waterproof, and very hard to resist hot dishes. Prepare panels as you would your furniture with stain, filler, and thin shellac coat, and then a coat of your sample. Allow ample time for drying and then rub to desired finish. Submit this panel to pressure and to 90° F. heat by placing a plate in an oven at 100° F. for an hour and then place the plate on the varnish over a cloth. If the varnish prints it is not suitable for table tops.

Other varnishes for ordinary rubbing can be tested for their rubbing qualities and ability to resist pressure without marking in a similar manner, but remember at least a week should be allowed after finishing before making the test.

NITRO-CELLULOSE LACQUERS

The test of lacquers is important. There has been a great deal of trouble in some factories as a result of lacquer blooming and turning gray after a few weeks. This is mostly because it is rubbed too soon.

Thinner for lacquer should always be purchased from the same concern making the lacquer, for the thinner must be in the same balanced proportion if the lacquer is to work correctly after thinning. Use of the wrong thinner will sometimes throw the cotton out of the solution entirely. Some finishers think they can make their own thinner and try mixing alcohol, acetone and toluol, etc., in various proportions, and of course waste more time and spoil more work than could ever be saved in this way. One thing sure to be remembered is that a great amount of lacquer on the market is little better than varnish for heat resisting and pressure marks. A real good lacquer should not mark from dishes, unless extremely hot, and pressure from packing should not mark it. Lacquers that mark easily contain a large amount of spirit soluble gums and not sufficient cotton film.

COLOR AND COLOR HARMONY

Every furniture finisher should have a working knowledge of color and color harmony. There are certain fundamental facts in regard to color that are invaluable. The normal colors are the colors of the spectrum, which may be seen when a ray of light passes through a glass prism. Blue, red and yellow are primary colors, and the combining of these colors produce the secondary colors, orange, violet and green. They are formed by combining two primaries, yellow and red producing orange; red and blue producing violet; and blue and yellow producing green. In addition to these are the colors known as tertiary colors, formed by mixing a primary and a secondary together. For instance, the product of yellow and orange is yellow-orange; red with orange gives red-orange, etc.

Luminous or warm colors are red, yellow, orange, light green and light tones of somber colors. The somber or cold colors are blue, violet and dull tones of luminous colors. Normal gray is black and white mixed in various proportions. Tones are gradations from great intensity, weakened by the addition of white or deepened by the addition of black. Hue is the change produced in a pure color by the addition of a smaller quantity of another pure color.

Color Harmony.—Colors appear different when placed side by side. For example, in a red object half in sunlight and half in shade, the red appears more brilliant in the sunlight as a result of the color absorbing the complementary colors, yellow and blue, in the sun's rays, and giving off more red or intensity of this color.

If primary colors are mixed in unequal proportions or of

different intensity, they will produce gray. Any given color may experience many modifications, so as to appear quite different from what it really is, according to the circumstances under which it is viewed. Make a test with red, for example, and note the following facts:—

Red, in contact with blue, appears yellower.

Red, in contact with green, appears purer and brighter.

Red, in contact with black, appears duller.

Red, in contact with white, appears brighter and lighter.

Red, in contact with gray, also appears brighter and lighter.

Thus the same red may appear many different reds according to circumstances under which it is viewed, being modified in intensity and tone. If a dark color is placed beside a lighter color, the dark color appears deeper in tone and the light color appears lighter. The quality of light, whether diffused sunlight, diffused daylight or direct sunlight, which illuminates the colored object, modifies the tone and hue of the color.

Color Modification.—A polished surface over a color gives a brighter appearance to any color and a dull surface the reverse. This is witnessed in the plumage of birds, and some flowers, like the pansy. For this reason nothing can be matched perfectly in wood finishing by staining, without first flowing a gloss coat over the stain and then making a comparison for color and shade. In matching an enamel finish, more care must be exercised in matching the color, for different number of coats, dull or gloss surface and light reflections all affect color. Many pieces are refinished as a result of not being able to match color for patching or refinishing of one piece in a suite. The age of the finish also modifies the color and matching becomes a difficult accomplishment. This modification is noticeable on both opaque and transparent colors.

SYNTHETIC VARNISHES

For some time synthetic gums have been used in tung oil varnishes of the quick-drying type, and are admitted as the finest varnishes yet to be produced, because they:

(1) Are less costly than nitro-cellulose lacquers, yet require but little more time in a wood finish schedule.

(2) Are print proof, grain alcohol, water and alkali proof.

(3) Dry tack free in 15 minutes, dust free in 30 minutes, to recoat in four to five hours, and rubbing after an overnight dry, in room temperature.

These varnishes should not be applied over a shellac undercoater, but over a synthetic or lacquer sanding sealer, which can be dry or wet sanded. Shellac may be used only when it is mixed with a shellac mixing lacquer. These sealers can be surfaced from three to four hours after coating, and a thorough sanding is necessary to give a smooth finish for the succeeding varnish coat or coats.

In thinning these varnishes, it would be advisable to obtain a special reducer from your source of supply, for turpentine is not a solvent for these synthetic gums.

While synthetic varnish can be used for all wood finishing purposes, it is especially recommended for tables of all types, dresser tops, store, bar and restaurant fixtures. Furthermore, it may be sprayed or brushed as the occasion demands.

SYNTHETIC-NITRO-CELLULOSE-LACQUERS

Since synthetic organic resins incorporate the same resilience and long lasting qualities in lacquers as in varnishes, lacquer manufacturers were not long in adopting them. Moreover, lacquers so made are free from that skinning over characteristic which is now true of the synthetic varnishes.

These lacquers require a special reducer, and in no case should ordinary thinner be used. However, the thinner for these is not costlier than the ordinary type, and should be purchased with the lacquer.

The method of application is the same as for other lacquers

with which spray equipment is used exclusively. However, they should only be used over a clear lacquer sanding sealer.

NEW DEVELOPMENTS IN STAINS

Through the recent development of a synthetic alcohol, known as methanol, a spirit color can now be completely dissolved without leaving any residue. This quality in addition to great penetrating power, makes it possible to coat over with varnish without any danger of bleeding.

The oil soluble aniline when dissolved in toluol can be added to either varnish or lacquer for a shading stain or coat.

Experience is the best teacher, and most finishers have learned that lacquer top coats should be applied either over a shellac and lacquer mixed sealer, or over a clear lacquer sanding sealer.

Mixing lacquer with shellac makes for a quicker drying and tougher film. Shellac if not strictly pure will leave a brittle film. A formula for shellac mixing lacquer sealer is as follows: ⅓ Alcohol, ⅓ Shellac, ⅓ Mixing Lacquer. This is cheaper than shellac or lacquer sealer, but must be sprayed.

Can varnish be used over lacquer sealer? It may require a special sealer, but mixing lacquer and shellac sealer would be better. Some varnish makers recommend only their varnish sealer for this kind of a job, particularly for table tops, bar fixtures, or restaurant fixtures.

CHAPTER IV

STAINS

NO GENERAL rule can be given for making stain formulæ for different kinds of woods that would be of much value to the finisher. Scarcely a piece of furniture that is made wholly of one kind of wood finds its way into the average home, and for that reason a different stain formula must be made for each kind of wood in order to match. A skillful manipulation of stain makes gum a good match for walnut, and birch is used more to imitate mahogany than anything else. Color is no obstacle in imitation. If the grain and figure are similar, the stain can be made to imitate perfectly. Do not try to imitate one piece by staining another piece that has a figured grain entirely different, as no imitation will be produced and it will only show poor judgment. Care must be exercised, if a cabinet has more than one kind of wood in the exposed surface, to know beforehand which wood takes the most color, as this should be stained last after weakening the mixture by addition of solvents.

The history of stains used today is a history of the coal tar aniline industry. This industry developed about the time of the Civil War. At first the dye was used as vat dyes for coloring fabrics. The dyes made from coal tar distillation are divided into three classes so far as they concern wood finishing: water aniline, spirit aniline and oil aniline dye. Some dyes which are soluble in water and used mostly this way are also soluble in spirits, as for instance, auramine yellow and Bismarck brown, which are mostly used in spirits. The manufacturer usually labels these stains as to how they are soluble. Some oil anilines are soluble in spirits. The finisher should be familiar with these colors, so that he may distinguish between them readily.

Stain being applied with cheese cloth.

CHEMICAL STAINS

Acid water stains formed one of the principal materials for use in staining before the advent of aniline dyes. Chemical stains are dangerous to use (many finishers would refuse to work with them), and they require more time to use than aniline dyes. Tannic acid, five per cent solution in water, produces a light brown effect, but is usually used on woods low in tannic acid content. A solution of bichromate of potash, 4 ounces to a gallon of water, is usually brushed over this to produce the proper shade of brown for walnut, etc. Nitric acid, sulphuric acid and picric acid in a twenty per cent solution produce a yellow shade on most woods. If used full strength it will produce brown shades. Muriatic acid will produce black and when reduced with water, will make any shade of brown. Bichromate of potash and carbonate of soda when dissolved in water will produce different shades of brown and yellow on different woods. Sulphate of iron will produce black on some woods and gray on others.

Permanganate of potash was the principal chemical stain of former years, and mixed in proportions of from four ounces to eight ounces to a gallon of hot water, would produce most all shades of brown desired for oak and walnut. Two or more coats could be brushed on if the first coat was not dark enough. Ammonia in strong solution is used for fumed oak. Fumed oak gets its name from the process of fuming by placing the pieces to be fumed in a tight room and placing therein a vessel containing strong ammonia. The fumes of the ammonia by chemical action give a rich reddish brown to the finish. Brushing ammonia on is next to impossible as the strong fumes attack the membrane of the nostrils.

PIGMENT STAINS

Pigments for mixing with water form a very small part of the coloring material for furniture, but distemper colors (ground in water) for graining can be obtained in the following colors:

drop black, Prussian blue, ultramarine, all the browns, as raw and burnt sienna, raw and burnt umber, chrome green, chrome yellow, English or American vermillion, fast red, turkey red, Tuscan, Venetian and zinc oxide (white).

These pigments are mixed with hot water, with a little glue for a binder, and usually a bit of aniline is added to give a true tone to the color, which is then mixed thoroughly with mortar and pestle or ground in a mill. Being opaque, they are of little value on close-grained woods, such as gum and birch where a transparent finish is desired. In fact they are not used except where an imitation of a figured grain is desired or for a gray effect on oak or walnut, using the white pigment to fill the grain.

Pigments ground in linseed oil or japan form the coloring matter for all paints and enamels and comprise the same list as shown in a previous paragraph, and many more, including the lakes and ochres. The japan colors are used when a quick drying color is desired. Below is a reasonable list of colors ground in oil and japan—enough for decorative use in the average shop or factory.

Chrome Yellow, Light	Prussian Blue
,, ,, Medium	Ultra Marine Blue
,, ,, Dark	Lamp Black
Yellow Ochre	Drop Black
Burnt and Raw Umber	Rose Lake
Burnt and Raw Sienna	Chrome Green, Light
Vandyke Brown	,, ,, Medium
Permanent Red	,, ,, Dark
Venetian Red	Zinc White, Flake White

STAIN SOLVENTS

No exact rule can be given for dissolving stains. The most important thing for the inexperienced to remember is that few stains of the same colors from different houses are the same in strength. A quantity of dry aniline of any color can always be obtained from any stain house, by submitting a sample for matching. Accurate tests for strength of color can be made by dissolving a given amount of color (say one ounce) into from one quart to one gallon of solvent. Value can be found only by comparison. This means that the stain giving the darkest shade of the same color with the same proportions of solvents and color can generally be considered the best value. This does not always hold good. For instance, if you have a straight brown aniline to match and ask another house to duplicate it, and find after examination that instead of being a true brown, it is a mixture containing an addition of nigrosine to make it darker, your match will only be temporary. If some of the colors fade faster than the others, or if you add some other color, such as red, to both stains, you will find they appear different again. If you wish to test a powder stain against adulteration or mixture, you can do this by saturating a small piece of filter paper with your solvent and blowing over this from your hand a small amount of the powder stain. Hold the paper close to your hand, pitched just a little toward you. You will find that the colors will all show up, if it is a mixture, as the small particles separate and fall on the wet paper at different spots. Of course, in spirit stains mixtures are necessary for many wood shades and a test of this kind is not always a proof that you are not getting good value or the proper color. Water stain and oil stain powders are also frequently mixtures.

Only in cases where you are offered a brown stain at a better price and represented to be a pure brown and found to contain nigrosine, is there an opportunity for complaint. Use water for tests on water stain, a denatured alcohol for spirit stains and benzole for oil stain tests. Dissolve a certain quantity of each color in the above solvents (given amount), keep these tests in air-tight jars, fully labeled with name of powder stain, from whom it was purchased, and the proportions of stain and solvent. Then you will have no trouble in making comparisons or keeping your stain formulæ balanced correctly. Nothing can be gained by having on hand several brands of stain of the same color and using first one and then another, and naturally never getting quite the same results. Stains are cheap and cover a vast amount of space (500 sq. ft. to a gallon) when mixed correctly and used judiciously. One good reason for using water stain is that oil or spirit stains will fade or change color on exposure to light.

A few formulæ are given elsewhere in this volume for producing the accepted shades on different woods, but most stains are brown or reddish brown. The proportions of powder to the solvent vary according to the color used and the shade or tint desired. As mentioned previously, you could first dissolve at the rate of four gallons of solvent to the pound of aniline and intensify by addition of black, or water for a lighter tone. Brown is the base of most stains and thus trying brown in the above proportion, you can shade to the desired color by addition of black or red, sometimes yellow, to give the color you want. This is applicable to any water, oil, or spirit stain.

The drying qualities of the different classes of stains differ considerably, and the penetration, evaporation and chemical reaction of the solvents differ. The stains dry in this order: spirit, water, oil. Under ordinary conditions, where the temperature averages 80° F., the time allowed after staining before the next operation should be: Spirit stains, two to four hours; water stains should dry in twelve hours, and oil stains in twenty-four hours. This is not an arbitrary rule. Many finishers do not allow this length of time for drying at any time and appear to get good results. Others are having trouble all the time with varnish not drying and checking as a result of not allowing sufficient time for stain and filler to dry. Factories do not take chances and allow ample time for drying to avoid trouble.

If naphtha (VMP), or 158-degree, is used in small proportions in spirit stains which have been dissolved with alcohol, the drying process can be slowed down considerably and easier application will result. VMP naphtha is also used with a mixture of C. P. benzole for dissolving oil aniline. Of late some use toluol or xylol (coal tar products) in dissolving oil stain, and these are reasonably slow drying, next to naphtha. In mixing the oil aniline, as shown in the next few pages, several items are used, such as asphaltum and rosin oil, not used in other stains. Oil Aniline is a derivative of coal tar distillation, and is one of the principal classes of dyes used in furniture finishing. All the prepared oil stains contain oil aniline stain for coloring matter. These stains are also dissolved in turpentine, benzine or benzole, as one of the principal sources of stains in small shops, being easily made and when dissolved with a solution containing a small amount of benzole, will penetrate the filler when refinishing.

Below is a formula for making a good brown mahogany oil stain, and the other stains that can be made from this formula:

BROWN MAHOGANY OIL STAIN

¼ lb. oil yellow	10 gals. solvent naphtha
1¼ lbs. oil orange	¼ gal. gloss oil or varnish
⅜ lb. oil red	2 gals. asphaltum
3¾ lbs. oil black	

RED MAHOGANY OIL STAIN

To the above formula add:
1 gal. of naphtha
¼ lb. oil red
1½ pint asphaltum

WALNUT OIL STAIN

To the original Brown Mahogany formula add:
¼ lb. oil yellow
1¼ lbs. oil orange
2 lbs. oil black
10 gals. solvent naphtha
¼ gal. gloss oil

GOLDEN OAK OIL STAIN

1 gal. walnut stain
2 oz. oil brown
½ pt. asphaltum
1 gal. of naphtha

When considering the effect of different colors on many different hard woods, it will be well to mention again that brown stain is employed more than all other colors combined. Oak is finished brown with few exceptions, never red, and occasionally silver gray. Mahogany was originally finished red, but of late mostly brown, and we see an occasional piece in Sheraton. Walnut is sometimes bleached and finished natural, or with a light brown stain and shaded brown. This wood was at one time the rage, finished natural with fiddle back, burl or bird's-eye figure to the grain. Birch is used successfully to imitate mahogany or walnut by using either a mahogany or walnut stain. Gum can be used in the same manner, except that the real dark gum does not imitate a red mahogany. Choose either red or white gum.

If a piece of furniture contains walnut, dark gum and birch, and an American walnut finish is desired, a great deal of testing will be necessary to get an exact match. The walnut is open-pore, the gum and birch are small pore. The same stain will penetrate further in the walnut, while the birch is very light in color and will need a darker strength of stain than either the gum or walnut.

The best procedure is to stain the walnut first to the exact shade desired, increasing the strength for the gum and still more for the birch. First, mix the formula with water, oil or alcohol as the solvent, taking four ounces to the gallon and then diluting, if necessary, to get the proper shade on the walnut. It will seldom be necessary to have a strong solution like the above on dark woods like walnut or dark gum. The addition of a trace of nigrosine in water or alcohol, or oil black to your formula will, with few exceptions, give you the proper shade for your gum wood and more strengthening with black will serve to match the birch with the walnut.

Of course, care must be exercised in the trial of these colors before using them, and the method previously mentioned, of shellacing over a small portion in strong light to test color, must be used to insure proper results. Be careful always in adding black to other colors, for little is required.

In many cases no stain is used on walnut wood and little on

gum. The filler, mentioned in Chapter V, gives the proper shade to these dark woods and especially when they are light in tone. Of course in such woods as gum and birch, where the grain is very close and little filler is taken into the pores, a stain is usually necessary. One thing to remember is that the filler will not change the color materially, but merely give it a deeper tone, and if your woods match in color before you apply the filler, there should be no material difference after its application. A little more color may be added to the filler, if desired, when filling the woods with a closer grain. The filler is made with a tone of the same stain color of a little darker shade. Factories have a standard stain color for the different woods and a standard shade of filler for each finish.

THE USE OF WATER STAINS

If one were to visit buildings where woodwork has faded out to a sickly yellowish brown, or notice the furniture or pianos in homes where light has faded out the stain on certain portions, causing a different shade from the rest of the piece, he would become an advocate of stains, proof against light.

Water stain should be used on all pianos, phonographs, radio cabinets, fine furniture and woodwork exposed to light, especially direct rays of the sun. Water stain should be used also in refinishing these surfaces when a practical and long life of finish is desired. Water stain made from aniline dyes should always be used under a lacquer finish to prevent the bleeding of stain by the lacquer. This cannot be prevented with any other kind of stain excepting the old chemical stains.

Mixing.—The only rule to go by and be sure of obtaining the desired results with water stain is to make your own formulæ to suit your individual needs. Many formulæ are given in different publications and trade periodicals for all the different standard finishes, but in order to get the desired results with these formulæ, you must use the same make of dye and chemicals as were used in producing them. This would require the names of the different manufacturers or jobbers, an impossible task. Most of these formulæ are given with the idea of selling a particular brand of stain, and if the reader wants these formulæ he can obtain them through the manufacturer or jobber of finishing material. Also, many of these formulæ are complicated and use several colors where one or two would suffice. How can you make a standard formula when different dye houses have a particular strength of dye in each color, some stronger than others, and in case of a mixed stain, many times the deep tone is made with addition of nigrosine instead of a stronger color? It is, therefore, impossible to give a definite formula that will work for all the different stains you are obliged to use from the several houses making or selling them.

A knowledge of colors and color harmony will greatly aid one in the matching of any finish with water stain. The manufacturer of aniline has greatly helped the finisher by furnishing samples of the different dyes for the finishing room. For instance, the following colors, soluble in water, are about all you would ever use, and some of these but seldom: Red (crimson), brown (tobacco), auramine yellow (lemon), nigrosine crystals (jet black), fuschine red (scarlet), malachite green (blue green), and standard walnut. You know that red, blue and yellow are the primary colors and that nigrosine will deepen the tone of any color by addition of small quantities of it to any formula. You could easily leave green and one of the reds out of the above list, for blue and yellow make the green. Yellow is seldom used except in the lighter shades of brown, and fuschine red, being very bright in color, is employed very little in ordinary wood finishing.

To give some idea as to the manner of mixing these colors for the average finishing job, say for a walnut of medium shade where quality is desired, water brown is dissolved in hot water, about four gallons of water to the pound. This alone will make an excellent shade for walnut. If a lighter shade is desired, a small amount of auramine yellow and water red can be added and the solution thinned down by the addition of water. If a darker shade is desired, add water nigrosine to this solution in a limited quantity. This stain may be applied to any wood where walnut stain is to be used and may be strengthened or weakened as desired. This stain can be used on mahogany for a light brown mahogany finish, and indeed, is used for most mahogany woods, there being very few red mahogany and dark mahogany finishes.

If a reddish cast of brown stain is desired for red mahogany finish, acid water red can be added to the above mentioned brown stain after it is reduced one-half with hot water. The reduction is sometimes necessary before adding any more color to prevent overloading the water with stain. The most economical way to dissolve stain is never to use more powder than can be easily dissolved by the solvent (water in this case).

If a light brown stain is desired, the addition of some auramine yellow to the formula and a weakening of the original solution will give this effect. This is sometimes desired for walnut for the reason that the wood is dark before the application of the stain, also for oak when a golden oak finish is desired. The original formula, with a little doctoring, is suitable for Jacobean oak, early English, fumed oak, weathered oak or Flemish oak, all being different shades of brown.

APPLICATION OF WATER STAIN

The application of water stain is sometimes difficult, especially where you must use short strokes and on panels where your brush comes up against abutments, for water stain should be brushed out and not wiped. Some finishers form a practice of wiping all stain, but this practice will cause dark streaks in the finish if you are using water or spirit stain. A long bristle brush with hairs reasonably stiff and from two to four inches wide, set in rubber, should be used for water staining. A brush with bristles set in glue will soon shed its bristles when the water has softened the glue. The same applies when applying alcohol stain. Take all drawers out of cabinets, also remove all movable parts and stain each separately.

Apply the stain in a sweeping stroke with the grain of the

wood, which nearly always runs lengthwise of the piece, keeping all surfaces horizontal if possible. Work back and forth with the brush without lifting until your brush becomes too dry to cover the surface well with stain and then dip the brush half into the stain solution and apply again as before, with the grain of the wood, back and forth, from the farthest edge toward you, until the surface is covered. Before the stain is thoroughly set, brush out without using more stain until the surface has assumed a dull appearance. At this stage stop brushing and allow to dry. Take the next piece and repeat this operation on it, remembering always to brush with the grain and cover all parts of the surface equally, to insure a uniform surface in color. Above all be careful not to cover the same surface twice, or you will be sorry to find that this surface will be darker than the rest, and will have to be washed out, or the balance of the piece must be stained over to match.

Carvings on refinishing jobs offer an obstacle to water stain, for the reason that the old finish is usually not removed well in the carvings. This also applies in frets, or grilles, and flutes or mouldings. Wire brushes can be used in these places, or steel wool can be employed, when the stain will not penetrate, and 3/0 garnet paper can be used to sand in stain on places that are flat. Just enough sanding to allow penetration of the stain is sufficient as more than enough sanding will cause a darker place. The sanding or rubbing with steel wool can be done after the stain is applied, and when it draws away from the surface, for in this way it can be noticed readily where the stain does not penetrate and can be corrected at once. Sometimes grease or oil is found to be the cause of the stain not penetrating; a little benzine or naphtha will clean this off before you apply the stain. Both sides of a flat piece, like a door or shelf, should not be stained at the same time unless special racks are provided for carrying them. At least one hour should be allowed before staining the other side and then it may be laid on a rack to dry.

When staining carvings or recesses of any kind, it is better to have a little less stain than customary, so that no surplus will be left when through brushing. If you get a surplus on any recess, pick it up quickly with waste or some absorbent material.

A little caustic soda is sometimes added to a formula to allow better penetration, but this is necessary only on removed surfaces. A little bichromate of potash can be used, about one to two ounces to the gallon, if desired, instead of the soda, and will be more satisfactory.

Sometimes it will be found that, after cooling, the stain will precipitate to the bottom of the container. When used again, the stain should be heated again and the container agitated or the stain stirred thoroughly. It will be found that the water will dissolve more stain when hot and for that reason the stain should always be mixed hot to get the full strength of the formula, then allowed to cool before applying, so as not to affect veneers or glue. Stone crocks are better containers for water stain than tin cans or iron buckets, as they are neutral chemically and the latter are not.

APPLICATION OF OIL STAINS

Oil stains can be applied with a spray gun or by hand brushing, but unlike water or spirit stains, must be wiped with waste or soft clean cloths. In mixing oil stain it is well to strain the stain before using, and after it has been thoroughly mixed, to prevent an insoluble aniline getting on the surface, for if this should happen, different shades may be noticed in the finish as a result of wiping particles of aniline over the surface when wiping off. It is better to purchase oil stains already prepared to give the desired color and results, and thus avoid difficulty. Most of the oil stain is purchased already prepared, even by those factories using large amounts.

Oil aniline can be made to dry slow or fast depending on the amount of slow-drying solvents used. When the surface begins to dry or show a dullness it is time to wipe off to prevent streaks. The slow drying of oil stains appeals to most finishers, and for that reason this stain is used in many places where water stain would be better. Little care is necessary in the application of oil stain except not to allow a slopping of surfaces where the stain is not wanted or to allow the stain to run. If sprayed on, any surfaces not needing the stain can be avoided by sloping the gun. In brushing care must be exercised at abutments or corners and the insides of drawers or cabinets.

When wiping oil stains it is best to wipe uniformly each piece and about the same time after staining to insure a uniform shade over all the work. When wiping the last strokes with the pad should be with or parallel to the figure of the wood. Wiping across the grain will leave streaks at times, especially if the stain is too dry. Very little instruction is necessary to get a uniform shade with oil stain, as wiping over twice will often tone up a surface that appears too light.

APPLICATION OF SPIRIT STAINS

While spirit stains are of little use in the factory, except for shading, if quick drying is a factor, and sometimes it is, these stains can be used on any finish over which is applied a heavy coating of paste filler or oil varnish.

The drawback to these stains in the past has been the difficulty in brushing them on without streaks, for they dry faster than one can apply them on large surfaces. This has been overcome by using the spray gun, and a very even surface can be obtained in this way. With the proper adjustment of the nozzle and air pressure, very fine shading can be done over the filler and previous to the finish coats.

There is no way to slow up the drying time of this stain without diluting with water, and this is not satisfactory, as few of the spirit stains are soluble in both water and alcohol. Naphtha could be added to those spirit stains that are soluble in this solvent, but in every case of dilution the shade of the stain will change and sometimes ruin the formula. Brushing on a large scale is therefore out of the question. Dipping of the stains is impossible on account of runs drying at once when removed from the tank. Small surfaces that could be dipped would be better stained in a water or oil solution.

The only place where the brushing of spirit stain is important is in refinishing and information is given in Chapter IX on this point. Spirit stain must be brushed on fast and not touched again. Lay the brush on the surface and pass across quickly and proceed to cover the whole surface as fast as possible. Never cover a surface twice, but use a smaller brush to touch up skips. Do not wipe.

DIPPING STAINS

Factories making chairs, smokers, and many small pieces can dip these in tanks containing either water or oil stain solutions. The time they are allowed in the solution should be noted and they should always be wiped when removed.

NON-GRAIN-RAISING STAINS

Below are formulas for mixing basic shading non-grain-raising type stains or dyes. They are fast to light, have good penetrating qualities and will not raise the grain of the wood.

BASIC COLORS: RED, BLUE-BLACK, ORANGE, YELLOW

Red Mahogany	*Brown Mahogany*	*Tobacco Brown*
2 parts red	2 parts red	2 parts orange
1 part orange	3 parts yellow	1 part black
1½ parts yellow	2 parts black	

Light Walnut	*Dark Oak*	*Golden Oak*
1 part red	4 parts orange	1 part black
4 parts yellow	2 parts yellow	2 parts yellow
1 part orange	1 part black	4 parts orange
1½ parts black	1 part red	1 part reducer

Amber Maple (or light oak)	*Cherry*	*Early Maple*
1 part yellow	1 part yellow	1 part yellow
1 part orange	1 part orange	1 part red
½ part black	1 part red	
	½ part black	

Brown Maple	*Wheat-Harvest*	*Sun-Tan*
1 part yellow	1 part yellow	2 parts orange
2 parts orange	3 parts reducer	½ part black
1 part black		1 part reducer

Use a graduate calibrated in ounces or milliliters for mixing and make a record of your formula. Though these formulas will prove satisfactory in many respects, the result will depend upon what basic dyes are used and the relative concentration of color in the basic colors or dyes. Each manufacturer has several yellows, oranges and reds to choose from. The formulas listed here were compiled using just one makers' basic concentrated colors.

The non-grain-raising qualities of stains of this type eliminate any sponging and sanding operation. These were first sold to factories for spray application and it would be best to apply them this way in order to control the penetration and the depth of shade. Permanent shading and touch up on sap streaks can be done by regulating air control and needle control in a very satisfactory manner. Their quick drying qualities make it possible to fill the pores and coat over the stain in about 30 minutes at room temperature. Of course, if the room is cold over a period of time after staining you may have to allow as much as six hours.

Use only special thinners for this stain to get best results. Acquire the thinner from the same source as you did the stain for all formulations are not the same. A pigment wiping stain may be an added operation in order to obtain the effect wanted or it may be used alone. Some manufacturers now offer blond shades of this stain to which pigment colors are blended with dyes to secure a semi-opaque or translucent stained surface.

Valuable tinting sealers and top coatings with transparent properties can be produced by adding the proper colors to clear spraying materials. Caution must be employed while tinting, as the concentrated stain is needed only in small amounts for this purpose. If a brushing thinner for these stains is used, care must be taken not to allow too much color when flowing it on with the brush unless one is quite familiar with this type of stain. It will be found that they offer a vast improvement in finishing.

CHAPTER V

FILLER

THE pores, or cells, of the wood fibre must be filled to give an even surface when finished, and as a smooth finish is desired on most furniture, it follows that we must use filler. There are two kinds of paste filler. One is new and is intended to be used under a lacquer finish. The oil paste filler, so common and used more than all other fillers, is a paste mixture of silex, or silica, ground with linseed oil, japan dryer, turpentine, and different colored pigments, such as the umbers and ochres.

Paste fillers are made in both quick drying and slow drying goods. The quick drying filler will dry within three to four hours while the original oil paste filler requires overnight drying before coating. The tendency is toward an oil paste filler that will not be disturbed by the lacquer, but any filler that can be dissolved by toluol or xylol (two coal tar solvents used extensively in lacquers for cutting gums) will always give trouble and require longer time for drying. For this reason it is advisable before using to test out all fillers, to see if the lacquer will dry clear over them. To do this use a panel of the same wood to be used in the major job, and after staining by the accepted methods, and after twenty-four hours of drying under good conditions, use a sample of the filler of the right color. Apply the filler and when hard dry, a good coating of lacquer—two coats will give a better test. If the lacquer dries within two hours and the surface is not cloudy, it is reasonably safe to use the filler for the job at hand.

FILLER AS STAIN

Wood fillers are commonly used for staining as well as filling the pores, and especially is this true in regard to walnut. The wood is dark and requires only a little stain to give the desired shade. Filler is employed also in two-tone finishes by using a

63

transparent or natural filler, with just a little color for the light shade, the darker portion to be filled with a dark filler. Oil soluble aniline can be added to the filler to darken it, usually brown or black.

Fillers are to be had in the following shades: natural, golden oak, light mahogany, dark mahogany, walnut, ebony and white. With the addition of pigments ground in oil or japan, any desired shade of filler can be made. Factory-prepared fillers are always standard in color and consistency, and the use of these prepared fillers is recommended. It would be bad practice for one to prepare his own fillers from the raw materials. It would be poor reasoning to suppose that a novice, or even an experienced finisher, could economically prepare his own filler with the same degree of accuracy as the manufacturer. It is only necessary that the finisher have a knowledge of what makes up a good filler, and how it is to be tested and used.

CRACK FILLER

There are times when a filler is needed for cracks and frequently it cannot be obtained readily. The following formula, to be used for a water mixture, made into a putty, can be put into cracks with a putty knife:

Mix thoroughly one pound of dextrine, one-fourth pound silex and one ounce of powdered glue. Keep this powder handy and when ready to use, add water stain to enough of the powder to fill the job. This filler will dry hard in a few hours and will serve well for small fillings. A good crack filler and also water putty can be purchased from most any supply house.

In the use of walnut, oak or mahogany fillers, about all the change that must be made is to add a little color in oil, usually burnt umber or vandyke brown, or for a considerably darker color, drop black or lampblack, to the filler to obtain the desired shade, mixing well before using. Oil aniline can be added also to tone up the filler.

The following oak finishes, when done the accepted way, do not require any filler, but are finished over the stain: Fumed oak, Flemish oak, Jacobean oak and weathered oak and mission oak.

WHITE PORE FILLER

Silver, French or Kaiser gray oak finish can be made by staining with a light gray or brown oil or water stain and then filling with a white filler. A thin wash coat of white shellac, about one or two pounds of shellac gum to the gallon of alcohol, can be brushed over the stain. After the stain is thoroughly dry, fill with the white filler. The shellac prevents the moving of the oil stain (oil stain is commonly used on oak finishes) when the filler is brushed on.

USE OF NATURAL FILLER

Natural oak finish requires a natural filler, the color of linseed oil, which is thinned and applied the same as any other filler. Many finishers prefer to buy the natural filler and mix their colors in oil with the filler, or if quick drying results are desired, colors ground in japan dryer can be used. This use and practice is the result of many different color combinations and a variety of finishes, so that it would not be economical to buy a different filler for each finish, as little of the filler would be required.

TESTING FILLER FOR SHADE

In testing out filler for shade it is an excellent idea to stain a piece of wood similar to the one you are to fill, with the same stain, at the time you are staining the larger piece. When you are to test the filler for shade, which should be as near a match to the stain as possible, apply the filler to a small portion of this and in about an hour brush over a coat of shellac, over-lapping the part now filled. Any material difference in the shade should be corrected by adding color or using a lighter filler. Trying to tone out the color in filler is a dangerous un-dertaking, as too much thinner will allow a quick precipitation of the silex and color, and a good filler job is not possible when filler is too thin.

Most prepared fillers are furnished with directions as to the amount of naphtha to be used to the pound of filler, but if no directions are supplied, one can thin to the consistency of a thick pea soup and just thin enough to brush on freely. Such surfaces as gum, birch, beech, maple and the evergreens do not need much filler, if any, and the filler should be made much thinner for these woods than for oak, mahogany or walnut. Most finishers shellac the first named woods after the stain coat and use no filler, as the pores are very small in these woods.

AGITATING THE FILLER

When the filler is the right consistency and the proper color, its shade producing the same or darker shade than the stain, as desired, it is ready for application. The filler should be mixed in a large receptacle, if much filling is to be done, and only enough for the day's work at hand or sufficient to finish the job, if a small one. The filler must be stirred very often, every minute or two to prevent settling, as the thinner at the top will not fill properly, and when you reach the bottom, it will be too heavy and tough and will not wipe off well or level.

APPLICATION OF FILLER

Use a stiff bristle brush, from two to four inches wide and with medium length bristles. The width of the brush, of course, depends on the size of the pieces you are to fill. After the filler is thoroughly stirred, flow on the filler liberally and brush out with the grain and across the grain in such a manner that the filler is forced into all the pores. Some advocate the brushing across the grain as the last operation, but this is not necessary if sufficient brushing is done to insure the sinking of the heavy particles into the pores. Finish with a light stroke with the grain. All surfaces can be coated to advantage if horizontal, as a heavy coat can be thus applied to such woods as oak and mahogany where much filler must be used in order to fill the wood properly. However, it is not necessary to do this unless you feel that one filling is all you expect to give the wood and you wish to be sure that this filling will fill thoroughly. Many

Application of filler. Surplus quantity applied to show a liberal coverage.

cabinet pieces are filled well on the tops and drawers, because they are placed in a horizontal position when filled, when the sides and frames are poorly filled and noticeable. The filler acts better on a horizontal plane surface than on a perpendicular one. Laying all surfaces horizontal would, of course, upset schedule in a factory, and for various reasons is not regarded as practical.

FILLING CARVINGS

Carvings sometimes are not filled because the filler tends to round the edges and fill the recesses too much, and it is difficult to wipe out such places. If the carvings are not filled, they must have at least one coat more of material than the rest of the finish and usually an extra coat of shellac.

WIPING FILLER AND DRYING

The usual drying time for fillers is from fifteen to thirty minutes before wiping, but no rule for wiping can be given, because the drying time depends on the amount of oil or japan in the filler and the consistency after thinner has been added. The more linseed oil added, the slower drying, and the more japan added, the quicker the drying. When the filler is too thick in consistency it will dry rapidly, in fact, too quick for a clean wiping. When the filler has begun to get light in spots or dull in appearance, one should begin to wipe off, using sea moss, excelsior or wood wool or burlap. Any material may be used that will not lie flat on the surface, but has a tendency to cut off the excess filler even with the wood surface. It is best to wipe first across the grain with even pressure and then finish lightly with the grain, being careful to get the filler wiped clean. Allow from eighteen to twenty-four hours for drying.

LIQUID WOOD FILLER

It is often necessary to fill oak twice and also mahogany at times, depending on the grade. Honduras mahogany is light and porous and must be filled twice. Usually the second coat is of a liquid paste variety, such as used on birch and gum.

Where a mill for grinding is at hand, the following mixture can be made for a liquid filler. A good mixer may do, but is not recommended:

To one gallon of good rubbing varnish add
1 quart of turpentine
1 pint japan dryer and mix with 2 or 3 pounds of fine silex.
The addition of a little corn dextrine will also help to make a good formula, but not over 25% in volume to the silica.

Fine sanding with steelwool.

Mix the liquids together and then add the powdered silica and dextrine, afterward adding color in japan and running the batch through the mill. Use just enough color to give the proper shade to the filler. This filler can be used on all close-grain woods and should be fairly thin when used.

ALTERNATING FILLER

In most cases where a liquid filler of reliability cannot be had, it is much better to give a coating of shellac varnish, as described in the next chapter. This coating will dry quickly and prevent suction of the finishing coats, or if finishing with lacquer, a spray coat of lacquer, with the addition of twenty per cent shellac, will suffice to prevent suction or sinking of the finishing coats.

CHAPTER VI

CHOICE OF FIRST COATERS

THE different materials that can be used and are used for a first coating on wood surfaces, and especially for modern furniture, are numerous. They fall into two general classes, namely, for the transparent finishes and the opaque finishes. For the transparent finishes, in the order of their usefulness, are the following: Shellac varnish (white and orange), seal coat (first coat varnishes) of different formulæ but containing oil and japan, but with varying amounts of different gums, and many different lacquers (wood oil and pyroxlyn cotton).

OPAQUE COATERS

Opaque first coaters are not so numerous, but cover a wide range of paint materials. It is generally accepted that varnish materials are transparent, but paint materials are opaque, and for convenience we will regard them so. Flat white from lead, lithophone, zinc, etc., is used extensively and colored with pigments in oil or japan. The best flat whites do not contain lead, as they turn yellow with age. They are usually termed enamel undercoating or paint primer.

Of course the first coater may be purchased in any color. Factories usually select a standard shade and have the paint factory duplicate it. In this way a special formula can be made for each factory, thus insuring it a shade or color that will be exclusive. Colored lacquers play an important part in the finishing department of a large factory and these consist of pigments ground in lacquer.

72

SHELLAC FIRST COAT

If a piece of furniture is to be finished in a shellac finish and waxed, it is plain that you should not use anything but a shellac varnish as a first coater. White shellac should be used on natural finishes of any light wood, from mahogany down to the clear maple. Orange shellac can be used on all dark finishes. This coater must be used over oil or water stain. Do not use it over spirit stain, as the stain will be absorbed into the shellac coat and smeared around, making a cloudy, streaked finish. This coating can be used over any paste filler, when thoroughly dry.

OIL VARNISH FIRST COAT

All the first coat oil varnishes, or seal coats, are applied the same as rubbing varnish, and the principal materials used in them are the same, namely, linseed or other oils, dryer and gums. On natural finishes a varnish with damar gum will be more transparent. Most oil varnishes give an amber cast to the finish. An oil varnish coater or sealer cannot be used with success over an oil stain without filler as the varnish will dissolve the stain and cause the varnish to dry very slowly and give a cloudy finish. This varnish may be used over water or spirit stain, but it is mostly used over water stain because it will dry better over this stain. This varnish has no evaporative qualities, but must oxidize, and any stain that will mix with it will prevent drying. If the paste filler has dried very hard, at least twenty-four hours, it may be safe to use this varnish, but it is best to use a wash coat of shellac over oil stain or filler before using oil varnish.

RULE FOR VARNISH FINISH

If you desire a varnish finish it, of course, follows that the first coat should be a seal coat varnish, or in case of being over oil stain or filler, a wash coat of shellac. If too heavy a coat of shellac is used for a first coater, all the pores of the wood will be filled and the varnish will not knit with the shellac. This condition results in chipping of varnish off the shellac coat, which is very noticeable. So be careful about your shellac coat, if an oil varnish is to be used over it. Make it thin, just enough to cover the stain and filler. The best rule is to use water stain, paste filler and a wash coat of shellac, and then a first coat of varnish. This procedure suffices for all varnish surfaces.

RULE FOR TRANSPARENT LACQUER FINISH

In event you wish a lacquer finish of a satin lustre, or dull for an ending, use water stain or non-grain-raising stain only. Fill with a special filler for lacquer and then coat with clear lacquer sealer or shellac varnish (white) for first coat. Oil or spirit stain will be absorbed by the ingredients of the lacquer and poor drying will result. Furthermore a cloudy or streaked finish will result. The procedure is the same for gloss or polished clear lacquer finish. If the filler is the right kind, the finish will really be better with sealers directly over the filler.

RULE FOR OPAQUE LACQUER OR ENAMEL FINISH

For all enameled surfaces a flat color must be the first coat, and if a piece is refinished and to be enameled, be sure there is no aniline that will bleed through the undercoat. This can be tested by spraying some of the material over an obscure portion a day ahead of the starting of the coating; this will reveal any bleeding and prevent a useless coating, for if it bleeds, you may be obliged to do all the work over again. When new wood is used all the precaution necessary is to select some wood with a very close grain, as maple, gum or birch. A regular lacquer enamel can be used as a firstcoater under the same material for second coat. An oil base lacquer undercoater is advisable on close grained woods.

SPRAY AND BRUSH METHODS OF APPLICATION

So much can be said about the use of the spray gun equipment that it is deemed advisable to treat this fully in a separate chapter. A reference to index will give you complete information regarding its use and care.

All first coaters can be used with an air gun and many of them work easier and form a much smoother coat used in this manner. Shellac and lacquer are two of the first coaters that should never be applied with a brush if a spray gun can be used. The reason is obvious—the fast drying of the film does not allow brushing over or lapping of the brush strokes.

SPRAYING SHELLAC OR SUBSTITUTES

In spraying shellac, or substitute shellac and other spirit varnishes, the products should be reduced with C. D. No. 1 alcohol to a right spraying consistency with low pressure, and the nozzle turned down far enough to prevent flooding the surface. Four pounds of shellac gum to the gallon of alcohol is the usual shellac formula, and with this for an example, you should reduce from twenty-five to forty per cent. The air gun should not be held too close to the work or the surface will be flooded. The distance will depend on the pressure and the consistency of the material. The nozzle of the gun may be held anywhere from six to twenty-four inches from the work, depending on the work to be done and whether the material is fast drying or not.

When you have reduced your shellac to the right consistency for spraying and have tried it for results on a separate surface, start spraying your surface. On flat surfaces begin next to you and spray with the grain from the left to right, past the edge, and back from right to left, dropping back each time just far enough to overlap one-third of the last strip. This overlapping must be done to produce a full coverage, as the edge of the spray feathers out and has little covering quality near the edge. The reason for passing over the edge each time is to prevent flooding the surface at this point when stopping to come back again. On perpendicular surfaces it will be best to start at the top and work down, slanting the brush down so that the sprayed surface will not be splattered by the over-spray of the gun.

All removable parts of cabinets or other pieces should be re-moved and sprayed separately. In case of panels in any piece it is best to spray the panel first, being careful to cover the edges near the frame, and then spray the frame by slanting the

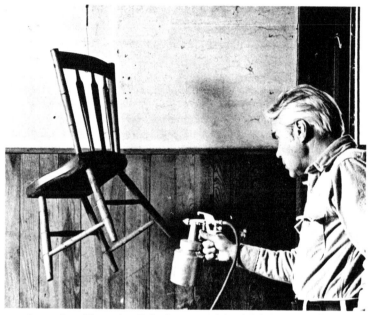

Spraying "hanging"chair to avoid sticking to surfaces.

gun away from the center and passing the spray all around the edge with the spray blowing away from the covered portion.

A coat of shellac is applied to the unstained surface or unfilled surface; this may be necessary also where other kinds of decora-tions or finishes are to be applied, to prevent the coating of that particular surface.

Care should be exercised when coating flutes, grilles, mouldings, or composition ornaments, as they will most likely flood and fill too quickly. These rough and raised surfaces will be well filled when the other coats have been applied, so little material is required for each coat on these ornaments.

Spraying of shellac or lacquer.

BRUSHING SHELLAC OR SPIRIT VARNISH

The brushing of any spirit varnish requires plenty of practice to get good results. It is inadvisable for an inexperienced man to try to finish a piece of furniture in shellac or any spirit varnish with a brush. He could not expect to get a smooth finish, on account of runs and sags, or a rough surface from brushing out after setting.

If the shellac is what is known as "four-pound cut" (four

pounds of shellac gum to the gallon of alcohol), reduce one gallon by the addition of a quart of C. D. No. 1 alcohol. This will give about the right consistency for brushing. Remember that shellac dries as soon as the alcohol evaporates.

SHELLAC TURNING WHITE

One way to prove why shellac turns white is to add some water to a shellac varnish and apply it. The film will be cloudy to white, depending on the amount of water in it. If you happen to be in some section where the use of shellac is taboo, as the result of so much rainfall, it is best to eliminate this product entirely and use some of the other undercoaters.

THE SHELLAC BRUSH

When applying shellac, or any spirit varnish, with a brush, be sure that you have a brush of the right size and bristles set in rubber. The average cabinet finishing requires either a two- or three-inch brush with medium length bristles. Some finishers prefer a soft fitch hair brush and others a Chinese bristle. A brush that will allow a quick flow of the varnish to the surface is best suited for fast drying products.

APPLICATION BY BRUSH

When brushing flat surfaces horizontally, begin at the side farthest away and work toward you, being careful to pass over the edge each stroke. Always stroke with the grain so that any brush marks will not be so visible. Notice in the illustration the correct position when coating with a brush. When starting coat the top parts of the piece and move down, taking everything as you go, so that you will never be obliged to come back to pick up a spot missed, and in that way drop material over a coated surface. If you should drop material on a coated surface, merely pass the brush over quickly to smooth out as soon after dropping as possible. The brush should be free from flowing material when picking up places or brushing out spots. Shellac cannot be brushed over at all after setting, so one must be careful to cover every spot as he goes along and avoid laps by going over it again.

Showing correct position in brushing any material. Upward stroke, beginning at the edge.

FACTORY PROCEDURE

Panels must be covered first and then the frame. The outside of drawers and all movable parts must be coated separately from the frame and not replaced until finished. The procedure in factories is to run the frames through and the removable pieces on a truck beside the frames; in this way every piece gets the same treatment by the same hands and, of course, will be uniform.

Downward stroke on perpendicular surface.

HOW TO LEARN BRUSHING

Practice with a brush with shellac thinned twenty-five per cent with alcohol, and keep up a constant stroke, back and forth, past the edge of a flat surface, until you can put on a coat on a space the size of a dresser top or davenport table. In this way you can become proficient in applying spirit var-

nishes to large surfaces. In covering round surfaces, go completely around, advancing up or down. In cases of flutes on turned legs it is necessary to coat the fluted portion first, using an up or down stroke. Carvings can be brushed in with plenty of varnish in the brush and then picked out with the brush empty of material.

In brushing quick-drying material near frames of panels or other abutments, the brush must be set down against the abutment and pulled away quickly toward the center; then set the brush against the opposite ledge and pull quickly to the center, lapping at the center before either has a chance to set. This, and many other operations when brushing shellac, require speed and accuracy and can be obtained only by practice and great care.

SPRAYING OPAQUE FIRST COATERS

Paint, enamel undercoater, and lacquer enamel undercoater and all the other opaque materials used as a first coat, can be sprayed with most air guns. The nozzle, of course, should be made to properly atomize these materials and a higher pressure can be used on the heavier bodied materials. Explanation for use of spray and its care can be found in a separate chapter. The same care must be exercised with the spraying of pigment coaters as with the spirit varnishes and the spray should be slanted away from the coated work always to prevent the overspray covering the coated part and spattering it. Work on horizontal surfaces from the closest edge, away from you and past the edge with each layer, and so overlap the coat each time in such a way as to secure a full coverage.

Hold the gun far enough away to prevent a pebble finish, and close enough to prevent a waste of material in the air, and a dusty surface as result of material drying before it reaches the surface. The pressure must be regulated for each individual material in order to get these results.

Some authorities advise crossing the work with opaque coaters in order to secure full coverage, and this should be done on the succeeding coats if only two coats are to be applied with spray. In case two coats are to be applied, it would seem advisable to cross the grain for the first coating.

BRUSHING ENAMEL UNDERCOATERS

A soft bristle brush, not over three inches wide and often smaller, must be used for enamel. Short bristle brushes of fitch and chisel type are ideal for a flat enamel undercoater. Of course no filler is used under this coat where the close-grained woods are used, such as gum, birch or maple. Some of the soft woods, as pine or spruce, are also used for enameling or lacquering.

The undercoaters for enamel are usually of the right consistency for brushing and do not need thinning as they do for spraying or dipping. However, if they do not brush out easily, they can be thinned with spirits of turpentine, but be careful not to add too much or the covering quality will be impaired.

Smooth, even brushing is required for undercoat enamel to insure a good smooth surface for succeeding coats. Look out for runs with this material as it does not dry fast and will run several minutes after it is applied. One good thing about brushing oil enamels or undercoaters is the ability to pick up runs and sags after coating, as the slow drying qualities permit long working. More care must be exercised not to coat any surface on the inside of the drawers or frame of cabinets or any other surface not supposed to be coated.

LACQUER UNDERCOATING

All lacquer undercoating known under various names such as pigment primers, lacquer enamel undercoaters, etc., are best applied with a spray. If necessary to apply with a brush, brushing reducer must be added to slow the evaporation and allow brushing out.

For clear lacquer finishing use a sanding sealer containing some transparent pigment. This material dries quickly, seals the pores against suction of finishing coats, and sands easily.

For lacquer enamels use as your first coater either a lacquer pigment primer or an undercoater, and when finishing breakfast or kitchen furniture made from close grain woods which are likely to come in contact with water, use an oil base undercoater made for use under lacquer enamel. These can be tinted, the former with lacquer enamels and the latter by addition of japan or oil colors. Japan colors are advisable as the material will dry quicker by their addition.

DRYING TIME FOR FIRST COATERS

Shellac, spirit varnishes, clear lacquers and lacquer enamels require from two to four hours for drying after the first coat is applied, and for best results, should never be recoated in less than five hours. Weather conditions have little to do with the drying of these products, but of course damp days will frequently cause a gray film to form on shellac or lacquer, and in some sections prohibit their use.

The stain or filler under these coats will determine, to some extent, the drying time of the above products. If water stain has been used, little difference can be detected between a surface on this stain and one over a bare wood surface as regards drying, and for this reason water stain or non-grain-raising stain is to be highly recommended under these products.

Undercoaters of pigments and oil, other paint materials or oil varnishes require from twelve to twenty-four hours, depending on the kind of material and the conditions under which it is placed when drying. Some of these materials may contain considerable japan dryer and for that reason dry much quicker. There are many japan pigments which will dry thoroughly within two to four hours, but they are rarely used except for striping and other decoration. They are used to some extent, however, under lacquer and varnish, and for speed. Overnight drying would be safe for most japan colors, but twenty-four hours would be the average for flat enamel undercoaters or varnishes made with oil for a binder.

It should be mentioned that most of the materials under this heading dry by oxidation and require a great deal of heat to dry within the time specified. A good enamel undercoat or varnish will dry in twenty-four hours in an even temperature of from 75 to 85 degrees Fahrenheit. If the temperature of the room falls below 70, you may expect the varnish to be tacky in this time. A good test for surfacing a coat is to press down hard with the palm of the hand for twenty seconds, and if no tacky or printed surface is noticed, you may proceed to surface.

SURFACING FIRST COATS

Several kinds of machines for surfacing are on the market. Some have attachments for using garnet finishing paper, steel wool, and felt pads. With such a machine large or small surfaces can be rubbed with ease. A pneumatic or electrically propelled rubbing machine that can be moved about on the surface with the hands can do as much work with one man as two or three men can do by hand methods. These machines usually have two feet on which may be attached steel wool pads or garnet paper and they oscillate as the machine is moved back and forth either across or with the grain.

If a machine is used on flat surfaces, care must be exercised as to the pressure applied, as many of them do sufficient work with their own weight. The directions should be followed carefully when using a new machine or when a new operator is using the machine. Most surfaces can be surfaced with the grain of the wood, especially the first coat, though some recommend first crossing the grain and ending up with the grain lightly.

Use of "belt" sander.

BELT SANDING

Many surfaces cannot be sanded with a machine and much work is done by hand in the factories and especially in smaller shops. Hand surfacing must be employed on uneven surfaces, except where it is possible to use a belt sander. The belt sander can be used on many surfaces that cannot be reached with an oscillating rubbing machine and included in these are the mouldings. The opposite cut from the moulding used, or the reverse of this cut, can be pressed against the belt and the sanding performed in this manner. Of course much care must be used on a first coat of material. Usually removable parts of cabinets are sanded in this way.

Another method is employed on turned pieces, and that is using the wheel sander. The wheel is turning at many revolutions a minute and the piece is placed in contact with the surface of the wheel, to which is attached garnet finishing paper of the proper grade. The surface in this way is smoothed quickly, but very liable to cut through with this method, as the pressure is hard to keep even. For that reason little of this kind of sanding is seen in sanding rooms.

The lathe furnishes not only a method of turning out wood, but of sanding as the piece turns in the lathe. The paper can be made to fit the piece and as it turns the paper is applied and thus the piece is surfaced very quickly.

HAND-SANDING FIRST COATS

The materials for surfacing are described in Chapter III of this section, and reference should be made to this chapter if any of the materials are unfamiliar to the reader. Suppose you are ready to surface either a lacquer or shellac surface as a first coat; it could be done with steel wool grade 0 or 2/0, but inasmuch as the object is to smooth as near level as possible, it is best, in most cases, to use dry garnet finishing paper. The reason for specifying dry paper is to make a clear distinction between this paper and waterproof garnet paper. The grade of paper varies from 4/0 to 6/0, depending on the roughness of the surface. The smoother the finish when dry the finer the paper to be used and 5/0 can always be used for sanding a first coater. It is obvious that waterproof paper is to be used with water and, of course, it is dangerous to sand a thin coat with water.

Hand sanding with the grain.

Sand all first coaters with the grain and do not lap the sanding more than necessary. A lap means more sanding on the lapped surface and little sanding is necessary for first coaters.

Sanding through this thin coat is very easily done. Edges are to be shunned. It is evident that an edge has little coating, and for the first or second surfacing, can be eliminated or touched lightly. Abutments can be sanded across the grain first as well as the ends of flat surfaces and then finished with the grain to make a uniform surface. Carvings are not usually touched until succeeding coats.

HOW TO HOLD FINISHING PAPER

Hold the piece of paper in the hand, or wrapped around a sanding block of felt or cork, and work from the farthest side, toward yourself, going all the way across the surface, with the grain, allowing each stroke to overlap the other far enough to make a full covering, leaving no part of the surface untouched. The paper should be held between the third and little finger and lay the hand flat on the surface. If the paper cannot be held firmly between the fingers, the palm of the hand should be made damp, and then the paper will adhere to the hand and not slip.

If the paper clogs up it is a sign that you are sanding a green surface, or else you are putting too much pressure on the paper, and the heat from the friction thus caused will melt the finish and clog the paper. When the paper refuses to cut, or has become too clogged with material, it is time to select another eighth-sheet and start anew. Do not wet the paper, as the glue size will dissolve and the grit will move off the paper.

The same method can be used for surfacing any enamel under-coat, lacquer enamel or japan coating. Steel wool may be used to advantage on all these surfaces where it is hard to operate with a stiff finishing paper. This applies to turned surfaces, flutes, grilles and carvings. Rub lightly and carefully with steel wool and have a pad with an even surface. This product cuts through edges just as quickly as the paper, so keep away.

CHAPTER VII

IT IS difficult to lay a hard and fast rule for the selection of second coat materials. So many different combinations can be made by using a coat much different from the first one, and of course the same material can always be used. By naming the most important combination, we can get some idea of the number of different combinations that can be made with this coat. Use the shellac varnish, for example. The same shellac can be used for a second coat, and it was often done by manufacturers who believed that this would give them the least trouble. Of course shellac has a low melting point, and is not waterproof, and it would seem to be inferior to lacquer finish in these two points, if not in others.

VARNISH OR LACQUER OVER SHELLAC

Lacquer can be applied over shellac with a perfect knitting coat as the lacquer will dissolve the shellac to a certain extent before drying. Oil varnish or the cabinet rubbing varnishes can be used over shellac, and this combination was the principal one for years. Factories and shops in many places retain this method of flowing a rubbing varnish over a first coat of shellac, which is very thin.

The shellac seems to give a good coating under a second coat of lacquer for the reason that the shellac does not soften quite as quickly as a first coat of pure lacquer, and makes a better filler for the wood, allowing a better and heavier film of the

89

second coat. Any spirit varnishes or lacquers, as well as any oil varnishes or enamels, can be used over a thin coating of shellac with good results. Varnish does not knit well over shellac, so it should not be applied over a heavy shellac coating.

OIL VARNISH OVER OIL VARNISH

No coat other than oil varnish can be successfully used over

Spraying with commercial canned spray paint.

a first coat of oil varnish. Of course paint or oil enamel can be used over a varnish coat, but this would be unnecessary, as a pigment undercoater would be the logical first coat for enamel. Shellac should not be used over oil varnish at any time.

LACQUER OVER LACQUER SEALERS

It is seldom proper to use any other material over lacquer, but finish up with lacquer instead for all coats. Of course if brushed, a pulling up of the first coat may result to some extent, and much care must be used in its application in this way, but if sprayed, you may be sure of a good application provided your air gun is in good working order and the pressure is correct. Varnish is often used over a first coat of lacquer sealer.

ENAMEL SECOND COAT

This material must be used over a good covering of undercoater to get good results. Two coats of a good undercoater and two coats of oil enamel will give an excellent job over close-grain woods. This should be used over birch, beech, gum or pine. Of course the enamel will not be the second coat if two coats of undercoater are used.

LACQUER ENAMEL COAT

There are a number of lacquers ground in pigment and some made from japan colors mixed with the lacquer, and these are known under different trade names which is quite confusing. Of course there is no law like the ruling of the Federal Trade Commission on shellac, saying that only such a material can be called "lacquer." Everything that has a nitro-cellulose ingredient is named as a lacquer and, of course, of many different formulæ. It would seem that some difference should be noted between a clear, transparent product and the opaque product. The transparent is called clear lacquer, but the opaque one is known as lacquer enamel.

A lacquer enamel should not be used over any other coating than itself, a lacquer enamel undercoater or an oil base undercoater, and in this rule you will find satisfaction.

SPRAY APPLICATION OF SECOND COAT MATERIALS

Much care should be exercised in preparing the materials according to the directions on the packages before attempting to use them. The spray should be clean and adjusted to the right spray for the application of the material and this tested on a separate piece before proceeding.

Spraying Lacquer Sealers.—A lacquer sealer is supposed to replace shellac as a first coat material under clear gloss or flat lacquers. The development of these materials are the result of troubles from use of early developed clear lacquers over shellac. Most of these sealers contain a finely ground transparent pig-

Any flooding should be immediately brushed up and re-sprayed to eliminate brush marks that show.

ment that gives body and allows easy sanding of the sealer coat. This first coat material is superior to any on new work under clear lacquer finishing coats.

Sealers are usually sold ready for spraying but on some occasions it may be advisable to reduce with lacquer reducer. In event of spraying during damp or humid days be sure to add blush retarder if any trace of blushing appears.

Always spray slow enough to get a wet coat on your work thereby insuring a smooth finish with little sanding necessary before recoating. Any flooding should be immediately brushed up and re-sprayed to eliminate brush marks that might show. Do not use over 50 lbs. air pressure for best results and be sure that the oil and water filter works effectively.

Spraying Nitro-cellulose Lacquers.—Unlike brushing, the spraying method does not leave the long streaky brush marks, and it makes little difference whether you spray with or across the grain. A piece sprayed across the grain for the first coat and with the grain for the second coat will usually show a better covered surface, as there is less chance of missing a spot by failure to lap the spray coat sufficiently. By crossing each coat a failure to lap on one coat will generally be covered sufficiently by the second coat across the first.

The pressure for nitro-cellulose lacquers should be just above or below forty-five pounds. At this pressure the nozzle should be adjusted so that a fine spray at twelve to fourteen inches away will give a six-inch coverage without pitting or dusting. If a fine dust flows over the work beyond the indicated covering coat, it is an indication of too much air for the size of spray or weight of materials. No rule can be given for the exact air pressure or adjustment of nozzle, but good work must be done at an approximate distance of one foot from the surface to be coated.

If a white appearance is seen in the coat, you must look for water in the air line. The work will never be satisfactory if oil or water get into the lacquer, as both are antagonistic to lacquer and ruin the coat. A simple separator for oil or water is described in Chapter III.

Always start at the edge nearest the operator, when spraying tops of cabinets or tables, and work away so as to prevent the overspraying of work finished. Do not zigzag, but follow a straight line across the work past the edge each time, holding the gun at right angles to the surface. Move along just fast enough to get a gloss coverage.

Spraying Lacquer Enamel.—This material sets up about the same as the clear lacquer, the difference being in the consistency. Some method must be found to agitate this material as the pigment will precipitate quickly. Of course if it is sprayed from a cup attached to the gun, no agitation will be necessary except when it is transferred from the container to the cup. If only two coats are contemplated, it will be necessary to spray each coat at right angles to the other and only thin the material enough to get it to spray. A low pressure should be used for this material as it dries quickly, and a heavy pressure will cause pitting of the surface.

Overlapping Spray Coat.—An overlap of from one-third to one-half of the width of the spray coat each time will be necessary to get a full coverage if only two coats are to be used for a complete finishing job. At least one inch on each side of a spray coat is blended out with a very thin coating, even where it seems to cover, so an overlap of two inches or more should be made on all lacquer spraying.

Spraying Oil Varnishes (Cabinet Rubbing Varnish).—A special consistency for spraying is made by the different manufacturers and this is recommended, rather than thin any varnish with turpentine or japan drier. Varnish is sometimes heated for spraying and, of course, it will flow much better if this is done. This material can be heated by steam or hot water as the safest method. Putting any material over a flame is a bad habit to get into—you may forget it and endanger yourself as well as others, and this is not allowed in most places as it is strictly against Underwriters' rules. When spraying a rubbing varnish or any kind of oil varnish, read the directions or follow manufacturer's recommendations.

Varnish can be sprayed as deliberately as desired, as it flows out easily and is slow drying. This material is not sprayed as much as the faster drying materials, for the reason that a heavier coating can be applied with a brush and runs can be picked up with the brush. If varnish is sprayed, a very light coat must be used each time, for the reason that it will run if sprayed on very heavy. Nearly all production shops using varnish apply it by spraying.

Spraying Enamel and Undercoaters.—Any pigment material

that is heavy requires a different type nozzle that is supplied for use with this kind of material. Manufacturers make these materials especially for spraying, and when purchasing, be sure that the material can be used for spraying or that you are supplied with the proper thinner for reducing it to the right consistency. The air pressure and material feed must be adjusted to prevent pebbling of the surface. The pressure must be higher for this material, as it is heavy and slow drying. The opening in the nozzle, of course, should be larger than for thin liquids.

The application of enamel or undercoaters with a spray is not essentially different than any other material, except you must remember this is a slow-drying material and the surface must be evenly covered but not flooded in any spot. A heavy coat or a hesitation with the spray will cause a run on any surface except horizontal, therefore great care must be exercised on perpendicular surfaces not to flood, and move the gun along at a constant pace without stopping anywhere on the surface. Always move past the edge, never stopping on the edge when dropping down for a new layer of covering material. It is well to spray these coats at right angles, especially on opaque surfaces.

BRUSHING SECOND COATS

To apply spirit varnishes, such as shellac or substitutes, or lacquers, in fact, any quick-drying material over a first coat of similar material, the material should be just a little thinner than material for the first coat and applied much quicker. Brushes for these materials must be medium soft bristles, similar to fitch, set in rubber, and be reasonably thick to hold a considerable amount of material, so that a full stroke can be made across any surface with one dipping of the brush.

Brushing Second Coat of Shellac.—The first coat must be sanded as smooth as possible, dusted off and cleaned up with a tack rag. Dilute the shellac to about a three-pound cut. Use a brush as described above, from two to four inches wide, depending on the size of piece on which you are working, and proceed to lay on the coat, beginning at the farthest edge and going across with the sweeping of one stroke, and do not brush out unless you have failed to cover or else left a surplus of material at some spot. Remember that the second coat will dry quicker, or have an appearance of so doing, as a result of penetrating the first coat to some extent.

On wide surfaces speed is the motto. Be sure to have your second brush stroke on the surface before the first is set, otherwise the second will make an overlapped surface by covering the edge of the first brush full and not blend as it should. There is no natural blending of one brush coat over another, and for that reason both strokes should be made as quickly as possible, besides a little brushing out to blend them to some extent. Be careful to go over the edges of tops after covering the surface and pick up surplus material deposited there by the brush when you rested the brush on the edge preparatory to beginning your stroke.

The frames of cabinets and all carcass work, except turned surfaces, are not difficult to coat with shellac or other spirit varnishes except where large flat surfaces, like table tops, are to be covered. There is only one system that will allow good work with shellac on large surfaces, and that is constant practice with much care and speed worked up to the point of being able to lay on a coating at top speed and at the same time not skipping any places or splashing material on a surface that has been coated. All removable portions should be removed and coated after removing. No one can do good work unless this is done. All drawers should be coated carefully on the edges so as not to overlap the finish on the inside of the drawer, as it cannot be wiped off like varnish if coated over another material.

In setting down a brush containing shellac, be sure that it has plenty of material in it and start the brush in motion as soon as you can, drawing it two-thirds across the piece to be coated and then go back from the opposite end, overlapping the first stroke. This applies principally on narrow surfaces where there is an offset or ledge to work from or panels.

Lacquer Material Brushing.—Be sure to read the directions

above on shellac coating and then read these special directions for the application of lacquer materials. There is little difference in the application of transparent lacquer materials or opaque pigment lacquers; they are both difficult of brush application as a second coat over the same material. The clear lacquer is less difficult over a shellac coating as it does not pull up the finish as much or sink into the pores as much as over a lacquer first coat. The colored pigment lacquer materials are usually brushed over a coating of the same material and there is little alternative as to what material to use, as they are about all of the same basic materials. Some are more easily brushed than others. It is simply a question of thinning out the material to permit a quick flowing liquid and putting it on as quickly as possible. The next quality to be developed is some material that will not brush up when the second coat is flowed over it and brushed out. It seems the only thing to do at the present is to develop a technique for distributing lacquer over a coated surface with the brush as quickly as possible and as smoothly as possible. It can be done and, of course, anyone can do it with enough practice.

Varnish or Enamel Brushing.—This is the easiest of all brushing materials, especially the varnish. You need not rush, in fact, you must not rush your work, as the materials require a good brushing out to cover the surface thoroughly. The surface must be sanded and dusted well and cleaned with a tack rag (rag soaked in oil varnish and hung up to get tacky) before it is placed into the finishing room for coating. The tack rag is the finest thing to pick up the little dust particles left by the duster, and any little particles of dust will leave a rough place in the varnish when dry. Sufficient dust will collect on the surface no matter how careful you are in cleaning up and sprinkling the floor and having all your clothes and tools free from dust.

For obvious reasons there is little difference in applying enamel or varnish, enamel being a pigment ground in oil with varnish and having the same general qualities as to flowing and drying. If anything enamel sets quicker owing to it being heavier material and cannot be brushed out as much. The next paragraph, on varnish brushing, can be referred to for enamel brushing.

Almost anyone can brush on varnish without getting a rough surface, but there are many things to keep in mind to get the right kind of a job. The varnish must be laid on with a soft, thick, chisel-type brush. This brush must be clean at all times and kept in a solution calculated to keep the brush in excellent shape. Seldom thin varnish for brushing. It is intended to be used just as it comes from the original package, and many varnishes lose their drying qualities or gloss by thinning. They should be right to use as they come, but in very cold weather

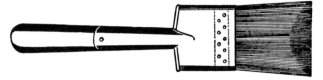

they should be heated by steam or hot water before using so they will flow out well.

Dip the brush in the pot and work it around until it is thoroughly saturated with varnish and then wipe on the bail or edge to take off surplus material and then apply to the surface, brushing back and forth and criss-cross until well worked into all the pores and does not pull away from any spot covered. After a surface is covered and brushed out well, draw the brush with the grain all the way across the surface at least twice to make the brush marks with the grain. Be sure that the brush does not leave surplus material to run down the edges or sides of a piece. Pick up all runs and sags and retouch all places skipped.

DRYING TIME FOR SECOND COATERS

Ordinarily one would not coat a piece the second time in the same day, but there are times when this can be done and must be done to speed up production or finish some piece hurriedly. All lacquer coatings, whether clear or opaque, can be surfaced any way in about six hours. Where forced drying is used, they may be surfaced in from two to four hours. The same is true of all spirit varnishes, as for example, shellac.

Oil varnishes and enamels are very slow-drying on account of the oils they contain which must dry by oxidation, and for this reason the drying time of these materials depends on the thickness of the coat and the amount of heat employed for their oxidation. In ordinary room temperature, few varnishes or enamels will dry for surfacing in less than twenty-four hours.

Synthetic gum varnishes known under various names such as 4 Hour Varnish, 2 Hour Varnish, Quick Rubbing Varnish, etc., will dry to recoat in four to six hours and can be rubbed the next day in ordinary room temperatures.

The test for surfacing second coats will be to press the palm of the hand heavily on the surface for at least one minute, and if no impression is made, you can safely sand or rub the surface with any material with the possible exception of oil and pumice. The oil has a tendency to soften a green varnish.

SURFACING SECOND COATERS

Shellac or Spirit Varnishes.—Sanding with dry garnet finishing paper, grade 5/0 or 6/0, is the proper way to surface this material if another coat is to be applied. Refer to the paragraph on dry sanding in Chapter VI for method of sanding. If this is to be the last coat, refer to the next paragraph on surfacing lacquer finishing with pumice stone FF and rubbing oil. It is assumed that a satin or dull finish is desired with a two-coat finish in shellac or spirit varnishes. Oil and pumice rubbing is about the only way shellac is finished.

Lacquer Material Rubbing.—If another coat of lacquer is desired after the second coat, use a waterproof garnet finishing paper, about 5/0, and do a smooth, quick job. This paper cuts off a surface quicker than any known abrasive and is very effective in skilled hands. A sponge and chamois with plenty of water are necessary when surfacing in this manner. Dip the sponge in water and cover a small surface at a time with water. Place a piece of the paper between the little and third finger and with the hand flat on the surface sand systematically with the grain of the wood, overlapping each stroke and working from one side of the surface to the other, keeping plenty of water under the paper at all times. Clean off the surface with the sponge and wipe off with the chamois to inspect. The operator can tell, after practice, when he has sanded sufficiently without wiping off, but frequent inspections are necessary for anyone not habitually at this kind of work, as the hand is not trained to feel a smooth surface. Much care should be exercised in sanding with waterproof paper, and above all, keep away from the edges until you learn how much pressure can be put on the paper when near the edge. Little pressure need be put on this paper for water sanding—it cuts fast. If the gloss is worn off the surface it is usually sanded enough.

Steel wool of grade 00 is used to a large extent in shops for surfacing the first coat of lacquer material and sometimes for the second coat, and especially when another coat is to be applied, but the waterproof paper has the advantage of making a smoother surface on flat surfaces and not clogging up as easily. Machines are made for rubbing with garnet finishing paper, steel wool, or pumice stone. These machines work back and forth the full length of the surface and many of the smaller type machines oscillate with two rubbing surfaces working back and forth and the machine is moved back and forth over the surface. Steel wool or a rubbing brush is used on uneven surfaces such as carvings or any surface that cannot be reached with finishing paper or any other surfacing material.

Pumice stone FF and water can be used for a second coat of lacquer material provided the coat is to be extremely dull or another coat is desired, and the same method of use, as described in the following paragraph on oil rubbing with pumice stone, except water causes it to cut quicker. With water and pumice a sponge should be used to clean the surface and a chamois to wipe dry for testing.

Oil and Pumice Stone Rubbing.—Select the proper grade of pumice stone and a clear rubbing oil. Have the oil in a flat vessel and add the pumice to it or else sprinkle the pumice over the surface after dipping the felt pad into the oil and covering the surface. Be sure the pumice is well distributed on the surface or pad before much pressure is placed on the rubbing felt, otherwise deep streaks may be made by ridges of material on the pad. A good smooth back-and-forth rubbing, lapping only when necessary, will produce a good satin finish. Oil rubbing must not be done in any instance unless it is the last coat. In production shops only a light sanding with fine, dry sandpaper to remove dirt nibs is done on first or second coats, and the main surfacing operation is on the last coat.

SURFACING ENAMEL OR VARNISH COATS

All the methods mentioned for the surfacing of lacquer can be used for either of these materials, and conditions have a great deal to do with the selection of surfacing material. It would seem logical to use a waterproof paper or pumice and water if dust is to be avoided and you are obliged to surface in the same room where pieces are coated. The use of water with any of these materials precludes the immediate coating of the piece, as at least two hours should be allowed in a warm room after washing off a piece with water. On the other hand, no dust will be flying in the air as is the case with dry sanding with finishing paper or steel wool.

Oil rubbing is to be suspended until the last coat, but if such a thing as getting a surface of any consequence is accomplished in two coats, you can surface with pumice stone FF and oil.

CHAPTER VIII

FINISHING COATS

IT HAS been customary to finish a piece of furniture with the same kind of material as the second coat, and with the advent of lacquer finishing, every coat is of this material, so that the only difference between the coats is the manner of surfacing.

SHELLAC OR SUBSTITUTES

If we take into consideration the finishing of furniture with shellac or other spirit varnishes, the decision would be to finish with this material if a shellac finish is desired. Of course shellac is not heatproof or waterproof, and for that reason is not used in most factories. It dries very hard, however, and seldom press marks, but will mark from hot dishes when the melting point is approached.

Any of the shellac substitutes are much less desirable for a finishing coat, although they do very well in some cases for first coaters. They are usually made from resin gums of low melting point, and while they rub to a very good finish, they will not stand hard usage and will mark easily.

The application of the finishing coat is the same as any of the preceding coats with the exception that more care must be exercised in spraying or brushing. Every spot must be covered and there must not be any sags, runs, laps or flooded places. There is no question as to whether it is best to brush or spray the finish coat, as the spray method always will produce the more even finish, eliminating the brush marks attending the brushing of spirit varnishes, and giving a better covering. However, if the spray cannot be used, brushing can be accomplished with good results if the material is thinned and great care and speed used when applying it. Coat from top to bottom, and if

102

using a spray on horizontal surfaces, start at the edge closest to you and work away to prevent overspray covering the finished work. With either brush or spray a good wet glossy surface must be had to be sure to have sufficient material on for a good rubbing.

RUBBING SHELLAC FINISH COAT

Shellac is a hard material to surface, and it is literally hard. Some object to using shellac because of this, but there is little difference from rubbing lacquer. It is better to sand with finishing paper of a fine grade, or rub with steel wool, to knock off the high places, if the finish coat has been applied with a brush. After the preliminary sanding use FF pumice stone and rubbing oil on a felt pad either attached to an oscillating rubber or use by hand, rubbing back and forth on the straight surfaces until you have produced the desired results. Wipe off the surface at intervals to see if the surface is rubbed sufficiently.

If rubbing cabinets that are paneled, rub the panels first and afterward the frames. All carvings and inaccessible places must be rubbed with a regular rubbing brush and little rubbing is necessary in places of this kind. Dip the brush into a mixture of oil and pumice and rub over the carvings briskly but very little in one place. When you have covered the surface twice, clean off and inspect. Benzine or naphtha are excellent for cleaning off pumice and oil and should be brushed on and wiped off with waste or rags. The rags or waste should be very clean and not contain any material that will scratch the surface. Wipe off with the grain when possible.

Wipe off straight surfaces with the grain, and under no circumstances wipe or rub in careless circles or across the grain. Remember the little mark or scratch made with the grain does not show, but across the grain is plainly visible, and so all rubbing must be done with the grain. It will require a great deal of rubbing with oil to get the same results as can be obtained with water, but water is not generally used on the last coat as it produces too dull a surface. Oil with pumice stone gives the satin finish.

VARNISH FINISH COATS AND RUBBING

Varnish should be applied over a second coat of varnish, so the specifications should read: Shellac, sanding, varnish, sanding, varnish and rubbing. This is the tried and true method

Using pressed felt pad in rubbing with pumice or rotten stone mixed with oil or water.

of getting an excellent varnish finish in dull, satin or high polish finish.

If sprayed on, the varnish should be warm so that it will flow out as smooth as possible without pitting, so in buying a varnish for spraying be sure to get one recommended for a finish coat. To get the best results it should not be quite so heavy as the second coat. If possible spray all the surfaces on a horizontal plane, for much running of the varnish will be noticed unless the operator is an experienced hand. It is frequently possible to get the most of any piece horizontally, especially the front, and all removable pieces should be laid in this manner. Spraying on a horizontal surface is likely to promote puddling and slow drying with an inexperienced spray hand.

It is well to use compressed air referred to in the previous chapter, to remove all dust particles on all pieces before varnishing, and when finished rush them into the drying room. Varnish should remain from eight to twenty-four hours, depending on the heat and drying qualities of the varnish, before rubbing. A good test for rubbing is to press the hand lightly on the finish, and if it does not mark in thirty seconds, you may rub with safety. A lot of varnishes used in production shops should not be rubbed in less than two to five days.

RUBBING VARNISH FOR DULL FINISH

To secure the dull finish use FF or FFF pumice stone and water on felt rubbing pad and rub the surface until smooth. Plenty of water must be used on the surface at all times to prevent heating and rolling of the varnish. Rubbing must be systematic and not spasmodic. Make regular strokes back and forth with machine or hand, as the case may be. Remember the machine was made to do the labor once done by hand, so use it whenever possible. Oil rubbing may follow water rubbing for a satin finish to prevent a grayish appearance.

Rubbing varnish properly requires constant practice, and while many may do a satisfactory job by following directions, few perform good work in a reasonable length of time without much practice.

Stay away from the edges until the last and then touch them lightly, for they cut through at the first touch if it happens to be heavy enough. The ends of any straight surface, where it breaks off abruptly, as the ends of dresser tops, etc., should be rubbed at first across the grain so that you need not press so hard when rubbing with the grain.

Round surfaces should be rubbed with a burlap or soft pad. Some of this is done on a lathe, as lamp stands, for instance. Carvings and other rough surfaces can be dulled sufficiently by a dulling or rubbing brush.

After the surface has been sufficiently rubbed, clean up with a sponge and chamois. This must be done as you rub to ascertain if the work is completed. Care should be exercised in the amount of rubbing to a given surface, and if you want to be sure you are not rubbing too much, count the strokes you make on one part of your surface, and when an inspection proves you have a good finish, then use the same amount of rubbing on the rest of the surface with the same pressure on the rubbing pad. This can be managed very nicely with a machine as the pressure will be the same, but using the hand method one is apt to relax the pressure or increase it at intervals, making an uneven surface. As said before, the only way to accomplish good results in rubbing is to do a great deal of it until you have mastered the stroke and pressure. Never make over two strokes across a table or cabinet top, but you can finish one side at a time, and changing to the other, make a lap on the strokes at the center.

SATIN FINISH ON VARNISH

This finish is by far the most popular of the three finishes. The dull finish may hide a multitude of sins, but it does not enhance the beauty of the grain, but rather gives it a dead look. The little we see of dull finishes can be traced to antique or imitation antique.

Highly polished furniture was the rage only a few years ago and it will come back again, for this is the only finish that brings out the full beauty of the wood. The satin finish is the most popular for other reasons. This finish is between dull and high polish, in fact, just off the polish. There are many degrees of dullness to this finish, and they may be varied by the amount of oil and pumice used. If a near polished finish is desired, add a little rotten stone to the pumice and use with oil. In this way a good polish is secured and yet have the satin finish from the fine scratching of the pumice.

A dull or satin finish is the series of fine scratches of the finish with the grain, and when made straight are not so noticeable. For an extra fine finish of this kind FFF grade of American ground Italian pumice should be used, and not the coarser grades of domestic stone. The domestic stone sometimes contains mica which will scratch the finish and ruin it.

Considerable rubbing effort must be put forth when using the fine grade pumice and rotten stone mixed because the cutting power has been reduced, nevertheless care must be exercised and the work cleaned off with naphtha quite often and inspected. The same machines, felts, stone and brushes are used for satin rubbing as are used for dull or high-polish rubbing. All carved or turned places must be hand-rubbed. Satin finish is the one used on lacquer, and this is the chief way this material is finished.

Varnish takes the finest satin finish of any material for the reason that the flowing out of the varnish and the absence of pinholes in the surface gives an excellent surface to rub. The finish should have a perfectly smooth appearance, without deep lines from rubbing, and no holes or shallows in the surface. Select the finest American-ground Italian pumice stone, of FF grade, and a clear rubbing oil of neutral or paraffine oil, and a woven felt to fit the hand or fastened on a wood block by glue, and proceed to rub all flat surfaces, concave or convex. The round surfaces and mouldings are usually rubbed separately and in a different manner. As mentioned before, rub with the grain and not across it, for the scratches are not noticed when made regularly with the grain.

The amount of rubbing necessary to produce the satin finish can only be determined by the appearance, and the piece must be wiped off for inspection after each rubbing to ascertain if sufficient rubbing has been done. Concentrating on any particular portion must only be done when it seems that the coating at this point is thicker than the balance of the surface being rubbed.

Frequently it happens that one begins rubbing a surface when it is a little too green in places, although the portion inspected for dryness seems in perfect condition. This occurs when some portion of the piece has been flooded with the spray or an extra quantity of varnish has been brushed on. When using the same material continuously it will be found that rubbing can be done within a certain limit of time, say, within twenty-four hours, and when a regular schedule is made, little trouble will be experienced in this direction. Where different varnishes are used from time to time, some experimentation will be necessary as one is not familiar with the product, and for this reason one should standardize on a good material and not change unless some advantage can be obtained over the material in use.

Machine rubbing offers all the same problems except that the pressure is usually even over the entire surface, but it is easy to allow the machine to rub through if not watched. The pad can be soaked with oil and sufficient pumice applied to it to cover the average surface of two or three feet square for one rubbing, but it is better to cover the surface with oil and sift pumice powder over it.

HIGH-POLISHED SURFACES

Today this method is too slow, and prohibitive on account of the high cost of labor. Of course many pieces are polished by frenching the surface with some of the many products for this purpose, but this is only done in a small way and the methods used by furniture, and especially piano, factories for polishing are by a process of rubbing with rotten stone mixed with oil or water.

OIL POLISHING WITH ROTTEN STONE

When a surface has been rubbed with a fine grade of pumice stone with oil it is very easy to wipe off and begin rubbing with a soft felt and rotten stone until a high polish is produced. Not so much care is needed as regards rubbing too much, for it is easy to tell when the surface is polished, as the rotten stone does not scratch, but merely by friction polishes the surface, and the cutting power is negligible compared to pumice.

Of course the same periodic inspection must be made in rubbing a surface, to ascertain if the degree of polish is attained, and it is best to make two rubbings for the purpose of polishing and clean off each time. After the first thorough rubbing, the spots that seem to be duller than the balance of the surface can be rubbed up to match the balance and then proceed with an even rubbing for a finish. One should be careful to clean the surface thoroughly when through. Oil rubbing with rotten stone is best done with a soft felt and brick rotten stone, as the brick is not so liable to contain dirt or scratchy substances which is sometimes found in the powdered form.

WATER RUBBING WITH ROTTEN STONE

Most all piano polishing is done with water, pressed felt, and rotten stone brick. When this is done the preceding coat is usually rubbed with water and pumice stone. If oil has been used on a preceding rubbing, it will be found more difficult to rub with water over this as water will not spread well over oil and you lose the lubricating power of the water until the oil has been removed and, of course, this requires more time.

The felt for water rubbing with rotten stone should be pressed, and for hand rubbing, about one-fourth inch thick. This may be attached to a block of wood for flat surfaces and a like piece used for rubbing curved surfaces. For machine rubbing a piece of felt to fit the rubbers is required. Plenty of water must be supplied to the pads all the time and rotten stone must be rubbed on the pads whenever necessary.

It is much easier to wipe across the surface with the palm of the hand when rubbing with water and thus clean a spot for inspection, and when the surface has been rubbed to a beautiful high polish, clean off with sponge and chamois.

RUBBING ENAMEL AND LACQUER

The rubbing of enameled or pigment lacquer surfaces for the finishing coat is done in the same manner as the rubbing of varnish or clear lacquer. The same care on edges, if pumice stone is being used, and the same frequent inspection are required to get the best results. The use of waterproof garnet

Using burlap for rubbing turned surfaces.

paper in finishing is sometimes employed and may well be used on pigment lacquers. The use of this paper with plenty of water prevents any rolling up of the finish, even though it may be a little soft. However, the best results in rubbing or sanding with any material can be had only with a strictly dry, hard surface.

If waterproof garnet paper is used for surfacing the finish coat, nothing less than 4/0 to 7/0 paper should be used. Take a sponge full of water and cover the surface with water. Have the paper on a felt or cork block with rounded edges to prevent cutting through at this point, and sand back and forth with the grain, overlapping each stroke with the previous one, enough to be sure of dulling the entire surface as you go along. Little pressure is needed with this paper for the cutting power is tremendous compared to pumice stone and oil, and the work can be accomplished much quicker in this way. Of course the work will have a very dull appearance and must be polished to some extent with oil and pumice or a mixture with rotten stone unless, of course, the extreme dullness is what is desired.

Machines are equipped to use this paper, both the large rubbing machine and the small hand oscillator, so no one need hesitate to use this material. This manner of hand surfacing is done almost altogether now in automobile, and to some extent, in furniture finishing.

FLAT COAT MATERIALS

In production work on cheaper grades of furniture we find much use of flat varnish, flat lacquer, and occasionally egg-shell enamel. The use of these materials avoids much rubbing, especially on the obscure portions of furniture and on office furniture, and yet give the appearance of a dull-rubbed finish. Flat coaters are applied usually with the spray gun, in the same manner as the gloss coatings, but care is exercised not to get any runs or sags to avoid rubbing or sanding. The first coat can be sanded if desired, but usually the coats are applied over each other, and not more than two coats over a coat of stain and filler are common.

The flatness of clear lacquers are the result of inclusion of some flattening agent such as wax or transparent pigment in a clear lacquer. These flat lacquers are made in various sheens, ranging from semi-gloss to dead flat. Most of them can be rubbed but should be selected with care if to be rubbed.

Flat varnish usually contains wax to produce the dullness, but it is preferable to buy a flat varnish that does not contain wax so that a rubbing varnish can be used over this coating if desired.

Care must be taken to get flat coat materials into corners.

CHAPTER IX

REMOVING VARNISH

REMOVING varnish and paint from old furniture is a considerable part of the finishing business. In many cities about all the shop work is confined to refinishing old furniture and transformations, like glazing and enameling. Even factories must remove varnish when goods are shipped back, due to damaged finish or special order work.

There is little difference in material or method in removing varnish, lacquer, shellac or enamel. Many good brands of solvent, or varnish remover, are on the market, and while most of them are disagreeable to use, few of them are injurious. If one uses rubber gloves with a pair of canvas gloves over them, all the precaution necessary will have been taken to insure no injury to the hands. A common formula for removing varnish can be made as follows: 40% benzole; 35% denatured or wood alcohol; 25% methyl acetone, adding ¼ lb. paraffine wax to each gallon of the mixture. The wax is melted and added to the benzole before cooling, and is then added to the other liquids and agitated thoroughly. This mixture must be agitated thoroughly before using to insure proper mixture of wax in the solution. Unless one is using large quantities it is not profitable to make varnish remover. Lye solutions should not be used as they do not have any advantage over solvents on the market and are sometimes injurious to the wood, and moreover burn up everything they come in contact with, especially one's hands and clothing.

There are two ways to remove paint and varnish with varnish solvents. A piece of furniture can be suspended into a tank of

113

the solvent or the solvent can be laid on with a brush. If suspended into a tank solution, an easier job can be made of it, but this method is wasteful unless the pieces are small and one has a great deal of it to do. It is obvious that a more thorough job can be made in less time than by laying the solvent on with a brush. But the saving of material does not amount to much, if anything, as the tank becomes loaded with waste material, and when it ceases to be active it must be replaced with new solvent. Paint and enamel require more time than a thin varnish coating. A piece should not be left in longer than is necessary to soften the varnish or paint and should then be wiped off very quickly with waste, rags or any other absorbent material.

If much removing is to be done it is advantageous to have at least two tanks containing solvent, and the last one minus any wax, so that when a piece is cleaned off the second time, it will not be necessary to apply a wash coat. The second tank must be covered tightly to prevent evaporation.

Most varnish removing is done by the brush method. All surfaces must be horizontal, if possible, when applying the solvents, to prevent the running of the material and breaking through the wax coating that forms over the top of the solvents to prevent evaporation. In cabinet pieces all drawers, doors, mirror frames (glass must be removed previous to this operation, also hardware), and in the case of pianos, all boards must be removed and laid in a horizontal position before applying the solvent. Most all cabinets can be turned into a horizontal position for all surfaces. When a piece is ready to cover with solvent, select a rubber-set brush, two to four inches wide, and having long bristles, dip into the solvent and lay on the piece, starting at the farthest point away and covering thoroughly until the whole surface has been covered, without skips. If the solvent does not remain soft at least three minutes, it is either a poor product or else you have failed to agitate it as directed to insure proper distribution of wax. Be careful not to brush the solvent out any more than is necessary to cover the surface, as the more it is brushed, the quicker it evaporates through the film and gives one little time to remove it.

The removing should be done when the coating is soft and not sooner. The only exception might be where the paint coating is so thick as to prevent a clean job with one application and must be repeated. From three to five minutes will suffice to soften the average coat.

In removing paint use a flat-edge steel scraper or broad putty knife to scrape up most of the material and a wood straight edge to wipe off all flat surfaces. Caution must be used with a sharp scraper on open-grained woods, as oak, walnut or mahogany, not to go against the grain, as a splinter might be taken out, whereas if the scraper is always moved with the grain, this cannot happen. It is not necessary to use a sharp scraper on varnish or lacquered surfaces, as the varnish should remove easily with rags or waste. Occasionally coarse steel wool is used in carvings or mouldings to scrub out the recesses, and a putty knife can be used carefully when cleaning out around panels.

A wash coat of naphtha is often used after removing, to clean up any wax that has been left on the surface. This is good practice, especially when one expects to use a water stain, as wax is an excellent material for shedding water. Flow on the naphtha liberally and wipe up with absorbent cloths as soon as possible, taking a small surface at a time. If lacquer is to be used as a coating, use lacquer thinner, never benzole, benzine or naphtha. It is important that all traces of the wax be removed from the wood before refinishing, otherwise it will prevent the new finish from sticking and may seriously interfere with the drying.

A sanding operation, while not always necessary, is advisable in most cases where a first-class refinishing job is expected and where one wishes to be sure it will not chip off later. Nothing is better than 3/0 garnet finishing paper for this operation. Sand with an even pressure, with the grain, the full length of the surface, moving from the farthest edge toward you with each stroke, until you have covered the surface thoroughly. Too much care cannot be taken in this sanding, as a spot sanded considerably more than the surrounding surface will take stain a great deal darker than the rest of the surface and the finish will be spotted. All the varnish or paint coating should be removed thoroughly before this sanding, so that it will not be necessary to sand one portion more than another: When working on rounded or carved surfaces, No. 1 steel wool can be used with good results.

REFINISHING

The following is a list of stains used in refinishing furniture:

Non-grain-raising Stains.—A liquid stain of qualities fast to light, strong penetrating, non-bleeding, and quick drying. This stain does not raise the grain. It is made in all wood shades and can be brushed or sprayed. Excellent to use under lacquers.

Water Stains.—Water red, water brown, auramine yellow, nigrosine crystals jet, walnut crystals, acid green, and methylene blue.

Spirit Stains.—American walnut, Bismarck brown, golden oak, fumed, nigrosine jet, auramine yellow and malachite green, stains which are soluble in alcohol.

Oil Stains.—Red, brown, yellow, orange and black are practically all the oil aniline stains used in refinishing.

In refinishing old pieces, the first thing to consider is whether it is to be a darker shade than the original or a lighter shade of the same color; or if the color is to be changed entirely or a lighter finish of different color.

First, we will consider making over a piece of oak, originally finished in golden or natural finish, both of which are light, into a Jacobean finish. The golden is a shade or two darker than the natural. After removing the varnish and sanding, prepare a dark brown aniline stain by mixing about one ounce of oil brown to one quart of a mixture of three parts naphtha and one part benzole (the latter liquid will allow penetration), and add color or naphtha as necessary to produce the desired shade. Try it out under a coat of shellac or varnish applied to an obscure portion of the piece. Be sure that plenty of light is on the surface when making this trial.

Second, we will consider making a brown mahogany finish on a piece once stained a deep red. This may be on mahogany, birch, maple or gum wood. On mahogany a brown non-grain-raising stain could be used after bleaching. If water stain is to be used on mahogany to produce a brown shade over a former red surface, use a straight brown stain (one ounce of powder to one quart of boiling water). Try this on an obscure portion and flow a little shellac over it to test for shade. If the red is killed sufficiently to give the right brown, add yellow for a light shade of brown, or black for a darker shade. Either will kill the red, and sometimes a little of both will make a more balanced mixture. Too much black and yellow will produce a green effect, therefore care must be used in making a color to go over another. Instead of bleaching, a neutralizing stain in light green may be used to produce the right brown. You may not be able to get a real light shade, but a brown can be had by using a small amount of acid green.

The same methods can be used for birch or gum, but often the water stain will not penetrate deep enough and spirit stain must be relied upon. It is very difficult to produce a lighter shade on any wood where the former stain has been produced by the use of acid stains for the reason that the acids unite chemically with the composition of the wood and penetrate to a great depth. This condition will be found on many antiques. If you fail to make a lighter shade by bleaching, it will be well to cease trying and make just a shade darker than the original finish, or if not spotted, you can finish the same color. Walnut is always finished in some shade of brown and can be bleached as a rule. Owing to its open pores it can be stained with either oil or water stain, also non-grain-raising stain.

Certain rules must be observed in the application of stains to secure easy application, true shades and uniform finish. It must also be remembered that the succeeding coats, to a large extent, govern the choice of stains. For instance, if one wishes to finish a piece of furniture in a lacquer finish and use nothing but lacquer over the stain, there is nothing else to do but use a stain which will not be moved by the lacquer. Any stain dissolved in alcohol, naphtha, benzole, etc., will be moved by the lacquer. We might also add that shellac will move a spirit stain, but not an oil or water stain. Oil varnish will move an oil stain, but not a spirit or water stain. Thus several combinations of stain and first coaters are possible.

As to colored woods it is obvious that any color must be darkened to obtain the same shade on a light-colored wood as would be produced on a dark-colored wood before darkening the stain. Therefore, either a red, brown or almost any stain mixture requires a stronger mixture of powder to the liquid each time it is applied to such woods as walnut, red gum, mahogany, birch, maple and beech, in order that the last named wood would be the same shade as the first. To make this a little clearer, let us assume that a brown water stain is made up for walnut, and it is desired to produce the same shade on a piece of mahogany. Add water brown stain to this mixture in liberal proportions or add water black nigrosine in a small amount to get a stain just enough darker to produce a brown on the mahogany to match the walnut.

Another important thing to remember is that new wood takes stain darker and much deeper than old wood, previously finished. For example, suppose an old mahogany dresser or chest of drawers is to be matched with several new pieces to form a bedroom suite. Stain the old piece first in order to produce the shade desired, as the new work will take the stain to any shade desired. The stain must be made much weaker, by addition of solvent, before applying to the new pieces, and then an accurate test must be made of both pieces in the same kind of a light to be sure the match is correct.

MAKING BROWN MAHOGANY OVER RED

Many finishers have difficulty in obtaining a good shade of brown mahogany over a red mahogany stained piece of furniture. A very easy way to get the desired results is as follows:

After removing the old finish, and sanding, prepare a very weak solution of water stain in green or else make a solution of yellow and add blue until you have a bright green. The mixture of these strong colors must be carefully made and the work must be tested until the exact shade is secured. Blue and yellow, two primary colors, if added in the right proportions to red will make brown. It is assumed that the shade of red on the wood is very light after removing and sanding, so too much emphasis cannot be laid on making a very weak solution. A material on the market known as a Neutralizer for Red Mahogany will, if properly used, change a red mahogany finish to brown or walnut. Sponge the wood with hot water, let dry and sand off the raised grain. Apply the water stain quickly and evenly over the entire surface. It is frequently necessary to wipe off with a half dry sponge or waste, partially wet, to get a uniform surface.

For testing color cover an obscure portion of the piece with a coat of shellac and expose to a strong light. If the shade is too green, wipe over a solution of bright red and test again, and if too light a brown, add either black stain or strong brown to the solution and go over it again. It is sometimes necessary to cover the surface with red to make it uniform, if sanded too much in spots. Use finishing coats as desired.

VARNISH CHECKS REMOVED

There are several materials on the market under such names as "amalgamater," "check eradicator," "knitteen," "flo-var," etc., for removing checks in varnish without removing the varnish. These materials can be brushed on any varnished surface, but the best manner of application is to spray them on. The surface must first be sanded with waterproof garnet paper, 3/0 or 4/0, using plenty of water. When this has been washed off and dried with a chamois, the surface will be cut up sufficiently to allow penetration of the liquid and at the same time clean the surface thoroughly. Allow six hours for drying before flowing the surface. When spraying or brushing these materials notice the effect, for most of them work better if not brushed out but flowed onto the surface as heavy as possible.

Finishing.—After at least twelve hours drying sand the surface with 5/0 garnet finishing paper and clean off well. Flow over this surface a heavy flow coat of a good grade of cabinet rubbing varnish, or in the case of dresser or table tops, use a very good grade of table-top varnish, in other words, a cabinet spar varnish. This last coat must be allowed at least twenty-four hours for drying at moderate heat, or more if finished where the temperature of the room falls below 75° F.

COVERING OLD SURFACES

To cover old surfaces without removing the varnish sand thoroughly with 4/0 waterproof garnet paper, clean off with water and wipe dry with a chamois. Allow four hours for drying before coating.

Following coats over old surfaces must be correct materials. Shellac or any spirit varnish should not be applied over oil varnish or enamel. Varnish, is seldom used over lacquer, or varnish enamels over lacquer enamels, neither should the reverse be applied, for instance, lacquer materials over varnish materials, unless a crackled surface is desired.

All holes or abrasions must be patched before coating over an old surface and just before the last coat (see Book I, on *Patching*). The same rule applies in coating old surfaces as in finishing new pieces, only the undercoat must be tested for the kind of material.

The turpentine test for varnish or enamel materials will result in the softening of such materials, whereas all lacquers and spirit varnishes will remain hard. Submerge a portion of the piece in turpentine spirits for twenty-four hours, or cover a portion with the spirits and the result will be the same, unless the varnishes are unusually hard.

Turpentine will dissolve wax and this can be removed by wiping with a rag, and then the test for varnish can proceed as before mentioned. Always sand an old surface before coating. If you feel that the surface you are about to coat is lacquer, and you wish to coat over it, the best way to decide the question is by coating over an obscure portion with some lacquer brushing material, and if it does not peel off or check, it is safe to proceed. Brushing lacquer has become very popular for refinishing old pieces of furniture and some information on its use will be timely. Do not brush lacquer material over a varnish surface unless you have a material that you know will work satisfactorily. On removed surfaces use nothing but water or non-grain-raising stain under clear lacquer.

Be sure you have patched the surface to be coated, as outlined and instructed in Book I, and that the surface is clean and thoroughly dry. Apply the lacquer as fast as possible, being sure to cover well as you go along, as these materials dry too fast for slow work and touching up. Be sure not to overlap any previous coating when working on a piece of furniture, and cover a small surface at a time without allowing time for setting of a brush stroke before applying another. There must be no recess when applying lacquer—stay with it until the job is finished.

Staining Over Old Surfaces.—The use of spirit aniline stain over old surfaces has long been the practice in cheaper work, and the best method of application is by adding to a coating of lacquer or shellac enough stain dissolved in alcohol to give the correct shade. Oil aniline can be dissolved in turpentine and added to varnish, or dissolved in toluol and added to all lacquers. These materials are seldom used unless the work will not admit of the cost of removing and refinishing. Pigment in oil or japan is also added to varnish or enamel coats. There is little to recommend this kind of refinishing, but the cost of some refinishing is more than the value of the piece, yet it is desired to change the color of the finish. In the case of oak made to imitate mahogany, it is necessary to use color in japan and added to varnish to give sufficient covering to hide the prominent grain of the oak. A more thorough method is to use a ground coat of red and grain over this before varnishing.

BLEACHING WOOD

There are many cases both in finishing and refinishing where it is necessary to use some form of bleaching solution in order to make the wood lighter. In the case of walnut, it is bleached to make what is known as the French walnut finish. Gum and oak are sometimes bleached before finishing, but the use of a bleaching solution will be of more use in refinishing where it is necessary to bleach the wood to make a lighter shade, thus taking out a dark stain.

The bleaching solutions are acid or alkali. The acid solutions are injurious to the lungs when sanding the wood afterward and the alkali solutions require some acid wash over them to neutralize the alkali so you can finish over them. If one will wash off the acid with water after bleaching and before sanding, the dust will contain very little acid. Bleaching lacquer may be used to bleach walnut.

BLEACHING FORMULAS

Oxalic acid crystals, dissolved in as much warm water as will take the crystals up in solution, make the best bleaching formula. One pound of sal soda in a quart of water makes another effective bleach. Peroxide of hydrogen is very effective on small ink spots or stains, but is rather expensive on large surfaces.

Application.—Any of these bleaches can be applied with a brush and allowed to dry. A second application, and sometimes a third is necessary in refinishing. The surface can be sanded off, but it is better to wash off the solution and allow to dry before sanding. Sanding is necessary because the grain will be raised considerably. After washing off the bleaching solution and before sanding, a very thin wash coat of shellac can be brushed over to stiffen the fibers before sanding.

CHAPTER X

FINISHING TROUBLES

CAUSE—PREVENTION—REMEDY

W HEN trouble develops in finishing operations the first thing to look for is the root, for without this identification an attempted remedy may serve merely to make a bad matter worse. Sometimes the real cause is difficult to locate, and a gradual process of elimination is necessary, checking all possibilities one at a time.

Once the source of trouble is located definitely it is important to know whether method or material should be changed to prevent a repetition. Frequently it is necessary to remove finishes that turn bad after going in service but many troubles can be remedied before proceeding further by simply recoating.

The following alphabetical list of troubles under the name by which they are known in the trade will cover the most common difficulties encountered in furniture finishing and even a theoretical familiarity with them will help when the actual emergency arises.

Bleeding occurs when the color of a stain or filler spreads up into a succeeding coat. For example: Oil soluble aniline stains containing red will bleed into and through either clear lacquer or varnish. There is a special coater made to prevent bleeding of mahogany aniline oil stains into oil or lacquer enamel finishing coats. A non-bleeding color is one which is chemically inert or not soluble in the finish coat, i.e., water or non-grain-raising stains.

Blistering represents the formation of bubbles or pimples on the surface of the dried or drying finish coat and may be caused

123

by excessive heat as from direct sunlight through a plate glass window or from a near-by radiator, or may also be caused by sealing wood that is slightly green, or a heavy coat of shellac over filler may seal in moisture from undried stain which expands when the finish is exposed to slightly higher temperatures and the moisture endeavors to push its way up and out.

Blooming appears as a bluish film on the surface of a varnish, lacquer or enamel film. A viscous rubbing oil, premature or excessively coarse or dry rubbing, inadequate ventilation, oil in the film from the spray line and chemical fumes are all common sources of the trouble. To remove, rub with liquid soap and rotten stone, then rinse with clean water and dry with a chamois skin. A bad case on lacquer should also be polished with brown liquid wax. Blooming differs from blushing, which takes place before the film is dry.

Blushing takes place in the film of a lacquer, shellac or shellac substitute during the course of drying when it develops a whitish milky appearance. Moisture in the air line, direct drafts, or a high relative humidity in the atmosphere, all may cause blushing.

In the latter case the air surrounding the work is filled to saturation with moisture, which is condensed on the wet film by the cooling action of the evaporating lacquer solvents. The effect is to precipitate a portion of the cotton which unless redissolved by the lacquer solvents reveals itself in the milky "blush." To clear up, spray on a coat of slow thinner like blush retarder, with or without a percentage of the lacquer. Lacquer Sealers, incidentally, have a greater tendency to blush than finishing lacquers because they are made "short" to sand quickly.

To prevent blushing, raise the heat of the finishing room to at least 70° F. and if necessary, change to a thinner slow enough in evaporating to stay in the film and completely re-dissolve the precipitated nitro-cellulose. Blush retarder may be added to ordinary reducers to prevent anticipated blushing, in proportion of one part retarder to three parts lacquer.

Bubbling commonly appears in the varnish film but may fail to disappear because of too heavy application, insufficient brushing or inadequately filled pores, in which air left in pockets works up to form bubbles as the varnish is setting, much as in blistering. A varnish that is green or very quick drying may also bubble. Bubbling in lacquer happens when the top film sets before the solvents have had time to escape. This results in the formation of small clouds of bubbles which are broken in rubbing, leaving them gray when the pumice dries. The bubbles are most commonly found near the edges where lapping leaves a thick film or when the lacquer itself is too heavy or made to top dry too quickly. Any lacquer which is not sprayed at the right pressure, held too close or too far away from the work or lifted near the end of the stroke, may also give this trouble.

In spraying clear or lacquer enamels hold the gun at right angles to the surface you are coating. Be sure that you are moving the gun fast enough to get a wet coat without flooding the surface at any spot. The gun must be constantly in motion. When you come to an edge keep on until just past it and return your stroke, overlapping enough to avoid skips or streaks between spreads of material.

Caking on the rubbing pad may be traced variously to insufficiently dried varnish, varnish on which dirt has been allowed to settle in drying or from which varnish skins have not been strained. It may also result from a harsh quality of pumice stone, from excessive heat generated by the rubbing machine block, coarse or "ribbed" rubbing felt or last but not least, insufficient water or oil lubricant. If the varnish is green, liquid soap may be added to the water, or rotten stone mixed with the pumice.

Checking is recognized when irregular lines appear in a finish coat upon drying, and is one of the various degrees or phases of "crazing," "alligatoring," "hair lining," etc. Inevitably a quick drying, over a slow drying or heavy coat will check, as well as any finish over a partially or top dried undercoat or even a single excessively heavy varnish coat, the top surface of which must necessarily dry first. In all cases the fundamental cause is an unequal rate of expansion or contraction in which the film of the least plastic element must give way to the extent that change in temperature is moderate or severe. Checking may also result after years of service from disintegration of the life of the varnish or in a relatively new finish by expansion of the wood following absorption of moisture. Lacquer is not likely to check over lacquer but may hair line over poor shellac, or of course, where specially made to "crackle."

Chipping describes a condition in which the finish flakes off the undercoat and is usually caused by coating varnish over too heavy a shellac coat or applying too many shellac coats. The varnish chips off because it cannot knit to the slick, glass-like shellac, especially where sanded very smooth. A finish that is not sufficiently elastic will also chip under hard usage.

Crawling designates a condition in which a finishing material will not completely cover the surface but crawls away and contracts at certain places. The cause may be a greasy, wet, waxy, excessively glossy surface or the application of a heavy material in a cold atmosphere. The remedy in each case is obvious.

Drying differs in its nature as between various types of coatings. The spirit varnishes or lacquers dry by evaporation of the solvents while varnishes or oil enamels dry by oxidation of the oils they contain, with the help of certain driers. Drying of varnishes, fillers and enamels is hastened by dry heat.

Grain raising takes place when a water stain is used in wood finishing, and the wood fibres are raised by absorbing water. These can be stiffened by coating the surface with a thin solution of shellac and when dry sanding off with fine garnet paper, or the wood may be sponged before staining with warm water, allowed to dry and then sanded, but it is risky to sand on the stain itself if the fibres again rise.

Greening is a condition in which the finish appears murky, due to too strong a stain application or the filler not being cleaned off thoroughly. This is also known as "Bronzing."

Lifting or *Raising* takes place when any finishing material applied over an undercoat has an effect on it similar to that of varnish remover. This is most often noticed where nitro-cellulose lacquers are applied over varnish or paint coats. It may be avoided by purchasing lacquers adapted for coating over varnish or paint, or by using undercoaters that are not readily affected by lacquer solvents.

Livering is a chemical reaction which causes a paint, varnish or lacquer material to take on a viscous, rubbery appearance. Varnish seldom livers alone and lacquers only as result of evaporation when container is opened, or when let stand with bronze powders. Livering in general is traceable to attempted or prolonged mixture of hostile ingredients.

Orange peeling is also known as "pock-marking" and is seen when the sprayed varnish or lacquer fails to lie down smooth. This may be the result of spraying the material with incorrect or without enough thinners, or of improper adjustment of spray nozzle, or using too much air pressure at the nozzle of the gun.

Pinholing occurs when tiny holes or pits appear in the wet varnish film before it dries. The condition is usually the result of improper filling of the pores in the veneer, or premature application of the varnish over insufficiently dried undercoats.

Pitting results when moisture or oil get into the air line and is mixed with the finishing coat as it is sprayed, giving it a pitted or ringed appearance on the work. The remedy is an oil and water separator attached to the spray booth.

Printing is brought about by applying sufficient pressure with or without heat to a varnished surface to make an imprint. It is virtually impossible to make a completely print proof varnish, but good print resistant articles are available and the rest is a matter of careful packing, avoidance of waxed wrapping paper, dead air summer storage, and proper finishing. A thin coat will be less likely to mar than a heavy coat. Lacquer finishes, while not entirely alcohol proof, are genuinely print proof.

Runs or *Sags* appear when an excess of material is applied or the material has been thinned too much. Pick up with a soft bristle brush all runs or sags before the finish has a chance to set and revamp method of application or thinning.

Sweating is a condition under which a dull rubbed varnish takes on glossy spots or streaks after being rubbed. Premature rubbing is the principal cause but too much varnish and the use of too fine a pumice stone may also contribute.

CHAPTER XI

NEW MATERIALS AND NEW FINISHES

THE following items will give the finisher the correct information on the use of latest finishing materials. They will be given in the order of finishing schedule so that you will not be confused in the proper sequence of each operation for a complete job.

ANHYDROUS LIQUID STAINS
Fadeless and Non-Bleeding

This type of stain is considered as the best all-round stain for wood finishing. Its process of manufacture is rather intricate, and because of the synthetic solvents used, they come in liquid form rather than in powder or paste form. They show good penetration even on removed surfaces, can be applied by spraying, brushing or wiping, can be shaded permanently, and dry quick enough to recoat in thirty minutes with any standard first coat material without the risk of bleeding.

Other advantages in using this stain: (1) gives the clearest finish possible; (2) does not raise the grain, and thus minimizes the sanding operation before the sealer; (3) will not bleed into the filler or other finish coating used over it; (4) makes possible a speedy finishing job; (5) leaves no sediment of consequence unless the stain has not been filtered.

Some manufacturers make standard colors such as red, blue-black, yellow or orange, making it possible for a furniture finisher to make his own formulae. This may be a benefit to the furniture finishing foreman in a furniture factory, for they frequently change their shades, but for the refinishing shops and the small buyer, it is advisable to have the standard wood shades,

129

such as walnut, mahogany, oak, maple, cherry and any special shades desired.

This stain can be obtained for making a red mahogany into a walnut shade or brown by neutralizing the old color, which makes it advantageous for piano and furniture refinishing shops.

DIRECTIONS FOR USE

Brushing: Use a soft bristle brush of camel, fitch or bear hair, which will hold a liberal amount of the stain. Flow this stain on the surface, leaving no noticeable laps; that is, do not cover the same surface twice, but work back and forth, lapping each stroke while wet so no lap will appear when dry. No wiping will be necessary unless you have runs, and if so, wipe with an absorbent rag. Many refinishing shops use the wiping method altogether since it seems to avoid all runs and sags. Clean rags must be used for this method.

Dipping: In production schedules, it is often advisable to dip the article you wish to stain. However, remember that odd shaped articles, such as posts, rails, carvings, etc., would not drain properly unless dipped before assembly. Special machinery is often necessary for these operations, and timing the operations is important.

Spraying: In applying anhydrous liquid stain with a spray, a number of things should be taken into consideration. The spray nozzle should be adjusted to this thin liquid stain, and the air flow corrected to the right pressure, else flooding will occur. It is also possible to shade any off color sap-wood to match the natural wood, a better method than using shading stains or lacquers after the finish is on.

Special thinners are made for this type stain, but a small reduction with synthetic methanol can be used without throwing the stain out of solution. If the stain separates, you will know that it contains other solvents than methanol.

UNIFYING OR PIGMENT WIPING STAINS

This type of stain came into vogue where manufacturers of radio cabinets and furniture used gum, poplar, basswood, etc., to imitate walnut. This type of stain dries slowly and can be wiped off to give the same effect on different woods, thus unifying them for the finish coat. The result can be obtained and controlled by wiping at progressive intervals, for example: walnut, red gum, poplar and basswood in the order named to get the same color on all. Each operation must be carefully timed to insure uniformity. These stains are not recommended for refinishing shops, but only for factories or where new woods of different kinds are employed in the same piece.

These stains are pigment base, but aniline can be introduced and varnish or Japan dryer could be used as a fixative agent.

Unifying stains are also used on cheap woods such as pine, fir, basswood, redwood and poplar to tone down a too prominent grain.

Sometimes non-grain-raising-stain is employed to unify the background, coated with a first coat of lacquer sealer, and then glazed over with Japan colors to subdue the light and dark portions of the wood. This is finished over with lacquer or varnish.

QUICK DRYING FILLERS

This type of filler is not radically changed from the old slow twenty-four hour drying type, but because it contains a quicker drying vehicle it cuts at least twenty hours off the finishing schedule. A small quantity should be applied at a time to avoid the labor of wiping it off after drying.

There is no question but where speed is essential this filler has proved a great boon in factories and shops alike.

DIRECTION FOR USE

When thinning, if desired, you can add some turps to the naphtha which is used to thin the ordinary fillers. Prepare enough for the job in hand, and any left over can be put back in the original container to be used again.

RECENT COLORED FINISH COATINGS

There has been a tendency to coat cheaper furniture with a unifying colored finish coat in order to disguise any natural defects in the wood. The great trouble with this finish is the fact that the bare wood is exposed when the finish has been worn or chipped off. It is almost impossible to patch this without spray equipment, and then not always satisfactorily.

This finish is usually confined to factories, but those who have old finishing jobs that do not merit complete refinishing can use lacquer shading stains, which can be had from most manufacturers of finishing material, either stain or pigment type.

Lacquer sealers can be colored, but since only certain aniline stains are suitable for lacquers it is best to make inquiry before using them.

Use a graduate for liquids and an accurate balance scale for the powders. Four ounces of most anilines make a gallon solution without settling out, but this depends on the strength of the color, so no set rule for making a stain solution can be given. Simply thin further with lacquer thinner, if desired. Strain this for any sediment and incorporate in the lacquer. Many tests may have to be made before you get the right formula. Lacquer enamels can be reduced to the point of making a translucent coating, very little enamel to much more thinner.

APPLICATION OF COLOR COATS

In most cases it is advisable to use a spray gun in applying either the varnish or lacquer type of color coatings, whether pigmented or colored with aniline. The gun makes a much more satisfactory job and also saves time. Incidentally it should be noted that some woods may need a wash coat of shellac or sanding sealer because of grain raising, and in this case it is best to use a clear sanding sealer, and spray the color coat over when the sealer has properly dried.

HOW TO MAKE COLOR COATINGS

Panel tests should be made on the same wood you intend to finish, otherwise the job may be off color. If there are many pieces to be coated at the same time in the same shade, it may be best to have a finish manufacturer make the coating special for the job, as their formula will always be the same. If you intend to make it yourself, use graduate, and scale for accurate record, so that future batches will be the same. It is best to keep a standard sample in liquid form so you can always check with the original before starting a new job.

Varnish sealers of synthetic quick-drying type are advisable if you are making a primary coat for a varnished finish. If aniline is desirable for transparency, make a formula as follows: four ounces of oil soluble aniline to a quart of VMP naphtha. Strain the residue with filter paper or charcoal, or many thicknesses of cheese cloth. Incorporate this in the varnish sealer, using a small sample only, and make a record of the amount of stain solution and sealer used so that the final correct shade will be your standard formula.

If you desire to use a pigment to make a translucent finish, a small amount of any given color in Japan will produce the correct result. For walnut you would use a mixture of burnt umber and Van Dyke brown, thinned with naphtha.

NEW BLEACH SOLUTIONS

There are a number of manufacturers now putting out good bleaching liquids with directions for their use. Some of these are intended only for new wood, while others are suitable for new wood and use in refinishing, to bleach or remove the stain in the wood before re-coating.

The result will not be as good from the use of these bleaches on removed surfaces, as can be obtained on new wood. Some are more successful than others, so in taking such jobs, do not give any guarantee of perfect results. One mahogany or walnut removed piece may bleach easily, but another may prove a disappointment. Results depend on whether the original stain was chemical or aniline, the latter being easiest to bleach.

One brand was tried with fairly good success on a walnut finish where the lacquer had been removed, but this panel was known to have only a filler, and no stain, but another example proved as successful where a non-grain-raising-stain had been used, and other tests proved disappointing, but satisfactory.

LATEST ACCEPTED METHODS

Generally speaking, a considerable amount of furniture is finished and refinished on a price saving basis, and in every instance of this kind, the finish will not be of the best materials or the best accepted methods. The two that are recommended are as follows:

Varnish: From a clean clear wood surface, properly sanded, use either an acid water aniline stain dissolved with hot water, or the non-grain-raising-type of liquid stain. Both are fadeproof, can be applied by brush, spray, or wiped, and in some cases dipping is desirable. When refinishing the latter would be more desirable because of greater penetrating qualities on removed surfaces that still contain oil filler. Use filler if needed.

The first coat commonly called sealer, would be the synthetic varnish type. This, of course, can be applied by brush, spray or dipped and sanded with dry 6/0 garnet finishing paper. The finishing coats should be of the latest type blended ambrol or phenol-formaldehyde gum with tung oil, made specifically for furniture finishing. Use gloss for body and quality, and sanding should be done with water-paper and rubbing should be done with FF pumice (Italian) and water.

This finish will be the finest possible and you will not find the cracking formerly noticed in the fossil type varnishes and also will be Spirit, food acid, and print proof.

Lacquer: The same stains are recommended under lacquers for they are fade-proof and non-bleeding. Any stain that bleeds into the finish destroys the transparent effect of the finish, and will wipe off. Both spirit and oil type aniline stains will bleed in lacquers.

Assuming that you have observed the usual rules in sanding, removing the finish and clean up before staining, in open pore woods such as oak, mahogany or walnut, a filling is necessary. Quick drying type of fillers are available in all wood shades to facilitate a quick finish by the lacquer system.

To secure the best possible results, free from crazing, cracking and water marking, a quality lacquer is important.

A sealer of the lacquer type with as little filler as is only necessary for sanding qualities, and not too heavy in body is desirable, and not too quick drying for better results minus blushing. Sand with 6/0 dry garnet finishing paper, dust off and apply top coats.

Gloss lacquer is sprayed over the sealer not less than two or three hours after applying sealer, use the desired number of coats, and run with water after several hours drying. Flat lacquer, because of the flattening agent, is not as resilient as the gloss lacquer.

Any finishing material containing the new synthetic type resin cannot be rubbed with oil as quick as with water. The oil has a softening effect on the resin.

NEW HIGH SOLID LACQUER COATINGS

These materials are a radical departure from the old type lacquers. They have high boiling esters, lowering the viscosity of the nitrocellulose so that a higher percentage of gums, of the synthetic type can be used, thus making a saving in coats, materials, and labor with less over-spray.

This material is obtainable in gloss and semi-gloss. This is an excellent product for retail furniture warehouses, and furniture shops, for it has the quality of not lifting a varnish finish, enabling you to sand out abrasions or packing marks, and spray over a thick coat, that can be rubbed in a few hours.

Shops using this product on antique furniture, save on the cost of the finishing job, for as smooth as it lays down, only a 0000 steel wool pad is used as the sole rubbing operation. Then, too, there is no blushing in relative humidity of 100° F.

NEW LIQUID STAINS

After long experiment, chemists have perfected aniline dyes in spirit and oil soluble that prove very good on extended exposures to sunlight. They are made into liquid stains under a number of trade names. They have good penetrating qualities, and while the spirit does not bleed into varnish sealers or varnishes, the oil would bleed in both varnish and lacquer.

STAIN-FILLER

Many manufacturers of medium or lower grade porous furniture use stain filler as a means of taking the place of two operations: staining and filling. These fillers are made by most manufacturers of wood finishing materials and are obtainable in several shades.

Essentially it is a combination of stain and filler and can be either brushed or sprayed.

It is very doubtful if this product can fully take the place of the two system of stain and filler for deep pore woods even from an economy standpoint; however, this would be a matter of opinion and may suit some makers whereas it would not be suitable for others.

For refinishing shops it has doubtful value but could be used in some cases for economy and uniformity of color even though the wood would also have to again be filled.

BOOK II

CHAPTER I

CEDAR CHESTS

CEDAR chests as produced today are intended in large part to offer a decorative appearance as well as to afford mothproof storage for furs and woolens. In consequence of this it is necessary to be familiar with three types of finish which are described herewith. In all cases no finish whatsoever is applied to the interiors and that on the exteriors serves the additional purpose of helping the aromatic qualities of the wood to be concentrated inwards.

Natural.—Where the chest is to serve a primarily utilitarian purpose, the finish is applied directly to the bare wood which is of a red and white streaked character. In order to harmonize the red more closely with the white it is customary to tone the latter to a pinkish shade by means of Venetian red in oil, reduced thin with benzine and applied with a rag. The next step is to inspect the surface carefully for knot holes which, when found, may be filled by burning in with stick shellac, sanded off smooth and level. The shade of stick shellac should blend with the color of the knot, generally a deep reddish brown. A simpler method is to shellac the hole, then make up a sort of fluid paste prepared by mixing rose pink and Van Dyke brown dry colors in varnish. This is knifed in the hole with a putty knife, cleaning off well around the edges, with a benzined cloth if necessary. It can be sanded smooth the following day if the varnish is a quick-drying one, or use tinted lacquer wood putty.

The next operation is to spray or brush on at least two coats of two-pound-cut pure white shellac. This shellac coat is essential, for despite much experimentation, nothing else has been found which will as effectively seal up the cedar oil exuded

137

by the wood. Moreover the shellac must be strictly pure—adulteration with rosin, copal or other gums will lessen its value and very likely result in a streaked finish, uneven as to lustre. It therefore goes without saying that shellac substitutes, varnish first coaters and the like cannot even be considered next to the wood.

With the drying of the shellac coat it is sanded smooth and finished with one or two coats of rubbing varnish or body lac-

Early American cedar chest.

quer, the latter sprayed, the former brushed or sprayed. The number of coats and quality of varnish or lacquer depends on the selling price. The cheaper grades are often given but one coat of varnish, rubbed only on the lid; the more expensive types are given two coats of varnish or three of lacquer, the last rubbed, on the top and front, with flat varnish or flat lacquer on the sides. Decorations are applied over the shellac coat and under the varnish or lacquer coats.

A peculiarity of natural finished cedar chests lies in the fact that on some the finish will seem to die away, as if by suction into the wood, in as little as six months, whereas other chests, finished identically, will show excellent body and lustre four or five years later. No adequate explanation for this phenomenon has ever been evolved, unless it be varying amounts of oil in the cedar.

Veneered.—For reasons previously stated, it is impractical to apply anything to bare cedar but shellac, beside which the strong red coloring and tight grain make the use of stain or filler or

Two-toned veneer chest of Acacia Burl, Walnut, and Bubinga.

stained shellac out of the question. Thus, in order to make of a cedar chest an article of furniture which will blend with neighboring walnut or mahogany pieces, it is necessary to apply veneers of these woods to the cedar. This is done over the entire exterior, and then it is finished exactly like any cabinet work similarly veneered and may be considered for finishing purposes, as walnut or mahogany furniture lined with cedar.

Painted.—The preliminary steps are the same as for a natural finish. Following the shellac two or more coats of oil undercoater and oil enamel may be applied by brushing or spraying.

The same number of coats of lacquer enamel may be substituted
if a speedier finish is desired. Decorations are applied over the
last coat, protected with pale varnish or clear lacquer. In fact
the system after the shellac is the same as for enamel finishing
on any kind of cabinet work.

Cedar chest with rare Marblewood veneer.

CHAPTER II

REFRIGERATORS AND KITCHEN CABINETS

TIME was when all ice boxes were finished in golden or antique oak with interiors of natural galvanized iron. The modern refrigerator is more apt to be made of steel throughout, finished internally in white and externally in white or gray, particularly the latest models of electrically refrigerated boxes. Nevertheless there is not yet complete uniformity, either in materials or methods, as will be seen from the various systems outlined below.

METAL INTERIORS

The interior of a modern refrigerator is usually of cold rolled steel. This is given a coat of synthetic baking primer to prevent rusting and baked at 300° for one hour. A porcelain liner is inserted over this when the box is assembled for shipment.

METAL EXTERIORS

First Coat.—This is the same as for the interior, but following the bake is sandpapered smooth and tack ragged.

Second Coat.—This consists of one coat of gloss white synthetic baking enamel, baked at 250° for two hours. No rubbing or polishing is required.

PATCHING

Light scratches may be repaired by spot spraying with a special gloss white spraying lacquer, obtainable from any lacquer manufacturer. Deep scratches or dents may be glazed with automobile lacquer putty, sandpapered and spot sprayed.

142

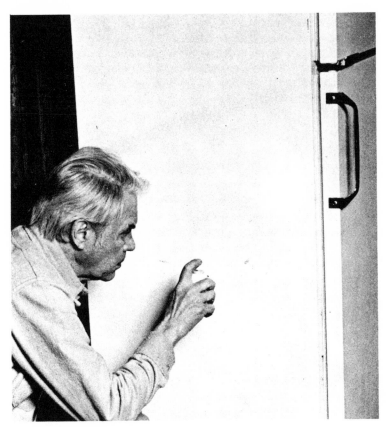

Spot spraying with commercial spray lacquer.

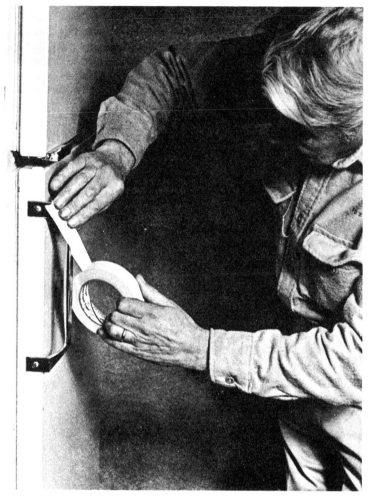

Care should be taken to keep lacquer from getting on chrome.

WOOD EXTERIORS

Varnish.—For transparent finishes oak, ash and elm are the preferred construction woods. All are open-pored so that if a natural effect is satisfactory, stain may be omitted and wood filler of light shade applied direct, reduced to cream consistency, brushed on with the grain and as soon as flatted, wiped off across the grain. In twenty-four hours this may be coated with clear or pigment varnish first coater and given twenty-four hours before sanding.

Over this one or two coats of waterproof coach varnish may be brushed or sprayed, and allowed to dry twenty-four hours before re-coating or packing. Or two coats rubbing varnish may be applied over the shellac for a high grade finish, the first allowed twenty-four hours before re-coating and the second thirty-six to forty-eight hours before rubbing with pumice stone and oil. It goes without saying that these varnishes are not ordinary ones, but are specially blended to produce maximum elasticity, toughness, water and weatherproofness. If desired a frosted finish may be applied, using colored lacquer or water stain, white filler and clear gloss lacquer to harmonize.

Lacquer.—First dip, brush, spray or wipe a thin oil-varnish waterproofing compound, full body, on all wood parts, air-dry overnight, follow with paste wood filler and three coats special waterproof lacquer sprayed full body at three-hour intervals. For a rubbed effect, flat lacquer may be used for the third coat.

Enamel.—Either the oil or lacquer enamel system for interiors may be employed, including the waterproofing compound and bond coat, but using only force or air drying, not baking, schedules. The bond coat is applied directly over the filler in the case of ash, oak or elm, directly on the wood in the case of birch or maple. Owing to the higher porosity of wood, an extra coat of enamel undercoater is desirable for oil as well as lacquer enamel. The finish color may be as for Metal Exteriors. Gum and birch call for waterproofing compound, two coats white-paint surfacer, air-dried overnight and sanded smooth, and two coats lacquer enamel, four hours between coats.

Backs.—For the backs of wooden refrigerators a sealer coat of any good ready-mixed paint will serve, a black or red oxide shade being usually preferred to cut the cost.

NOTES ON REFRIGERATOR FINISHING

All coats should be given plenty of time to dry under natural conditions, but artificial heat up to 100–110° F. with proper humidity control, will hasten the schedule without danger.

A long-oil varnish is preferable to a varnish artificially made to dry quickly; the latter is liable to be brittle and will not anchor as well. Wherever encountered end grain should be sealed with glazing compound, knifed well in and smoothed off. Parts recessed for hinges should be varnished as well as the edges of glass to help the putty stick. See that every place that moisture might enter wood or metal is perfectly sealed.

KITCHEN CABINETS

Metal.—The same system as for refrigerator metal exteriors.

Wood, Enamel.—The service conditions being less severe than with refrigerators, one or two coats each of oil primer, undercoater and gloss or eggshell enamel will serve, air or force dried, in white or light colors with conventional stencil decorations on panels.

Wood, Stain.—In line with the tendency to increase the decorativeness of kitchen furnishings, oak cabinets are being turned out finished in gray or brown lacquer or stain effects, as described under *Breakfast Room Furniture* in this book. and *Flat Frosting*, as described in Book II, Chapter V. Additional decoration may consist of vein lining or two-toning. Cheaper cabinets may be finished with combination wood filler, varnish pigment firstcoater and flat varnish, one coat each.

CHAPTER III

WICKER FURNITURE

WICKER is the general term applied to furniture which is of the woven rather than solid or veneered smooth type. The strands used in the cheaper grades are "fibre" reed, which means coarse, tough paper twisted spirally to great toughness; the more expensive grades are of natural willow, reed or rattan, treated by steam to soften them for plaiting and braiding. While the finish effect is the same for both, the difference in character of the two grades is such that distinct treatments are necessary for each, alike for stain and enamel.

STAINING FIBRE REED

Owing to the porosity of even the toughest paper it is necessary to apply a stiff preliminary coating which will cause it to hold out the finish. For a natural finish the paper twistings (fibre) are dipped in thin water glue; or the paper strips may first be dyed in aniline water stains, twisted, glue-sized and interwoven on the frame in a two-, three- or four-color pattern. All work is done by machinery up to the finish coats.

If already shaped and assembled uncoated, the stain may be brushed, sprayed or dipped, after which the piece is dipped in the glue size and dried for 24 hours. For a brown mahogany effect, a solution of about five ounces Adam. brown aniline dry powder to the gallon of hot water is used; for a light brown, one to three ounces of standard brown aniline; for light gray, one ounce jet nigrosine. The number and shade of possible stain effects is limited only by the proportions of red, brown, black, green, blue and yellow aniline powders used to the gallon of water. Oil stain may also be used, but it does not dry as satis-

147

factorily nor is it as clear in tone as the water, nor permanent in color.

The piece is now ready for a dip, spray or brush coat of tough, pale, elastic waterproof coach varnish to dry dust free in three or four hours and hard overnight.

STAINING WILLOW REED

The process is the same as for fibre except that no glue size is required and staining starts after the piece is assembled, a little alcohol being added to the water stain to aid penetration.

It is best to singe off "whiskers" with flame before finishing.

Rattan is even less porous than willow and is therefore not often stained, usually being left natural or finished with a thin coat ᴏ𝚏 pale varnish. It is customary first to singe off the "whiskers" with a mild flame before finishing.

OIL ENAMEL ON FIBRE AND WILLOW

Fibre may first be glue-sized as previously described, then worked into shape, but willow is steamed and shaped without sizing. The first step is to spray on a coat of flat paint undercoater tinted to the finish color and thinned with a little turpentine to aid penetration. A brush may be used instead of a spray, but this method is not nearly as quick or thorough.

It is not, of course, possible to sand the undercoater, for which reason a very finely ground type is required which will lie smooth. Fibre calls for two coats; willow being less porous, needs but one, after which a finishing coat of elastic high grade gloss enamel is sprayed on. Some manufacturers use but one coat of primer and one of enamel, others two coats of enamel and one of primer, still others two coats of enamel only, the first reduced somewhat with turpentine. These variations depend largely on the selling price, on the character of materials and the amount of time it is desired to put into the finishing operations.

SPECIAL OIL ENAMEL FOR FROSTING

Where the enamel is to be frosted, and practically all wicker furniture at some time is, the above methods are apt to require considerable time, since it is essential that all coats, especially the last one, be hard dry lest the frosting color penetrate and blur instead of wiping off clean and smooth. To overcome this, special "two-toning" enamels have been constructed to top dry with extra speed but without sacrifice of elasticity. Such enamels may be safely frosted in from five to eight hours and will give fully as durable service as the standard type.

LACQUER ENAMEL ON FIBRE AND WILLOW

The advent of nitro-cellulose lacquers has made it possible to finish up wicker furniture complete for frosting in from twenty-four to thirty-six hours. A special elastic lacquer primer should be employed, followed by one or two coats of lacquer enamel, but many think it better and cheaper in the case of glue-sized fibre to employ a paint undercoater of a type adapted to use under lacquer, allowing it to dry twenty-four hours, followed by a coat either of colored or clear lacquer. Naturally oil or oil and japan frosting colors may be applied to lacquer enamel with safety in an hour or less, and lacquer enamel may be applied to willow with either clear lacquer primer or no primer at all. Spraying is preferable to dipping or brushing.

BRONZE FINISHES

A bronze finish on wicker furniture may be produced in two ways. If the bronzing liquid be varnish, it is best to seal it

Spraying wicker.

with a coat of shellac substitute before frosting. The speedier method is to use a lacquer bronzing liquid for the metallic powders, as no intermediate shellac coat is necessary before applying the frosting color which may also be applied much sooner. Bronze finishes on wicker furniture are often antique glazed, which should have a protecting clear coat.

PATTERN TWO-TONING AND SHADING

As a variation from frosting wicker furniture, it is often banded or two-toned, by applying an enamel color of harmonious or contrasting shade to the plaited band running along the front of a chair seat, or over the arms and back, around the top of a table, the feet or legs, or even on a design woven in the back or front of a chair or settee or in a table top. This latter must be done with care by means of a pencil brush, but of course is not necessary if the fibre has been colored previous to weaving in the pattern.

CHAPTER IV

THE production finishing of radio cabinets depends in the main on three factors: the wood, production facilities, and grade. High priced cabinets show fancy veneers and are finished exactly like furniture of comparable quality. Cheaper cabinets are walnut veneered on fronts; otherwise, the wood

Mahogany cassette case.

is gum or poplar. These are in the vast majority and are finished as follows:

STAINING

When received from the cabinet room the gum parts are

152

Mahogany stereo cabinet with inlaid trim.

Stereo in cherry cabinet.

spray stained with non-grain-raising stain in light or medium walnut shades and the walnut veneer misted with the same stain. The reason for this misting is that the gum parts being

Mahogany speaker box.

spray stained with non-grain-raising stain in light or medium walnut shades and the walnut veneer misted with the same stain.

Walnut speaker box.

FILLING

The next operation calls for paste wood filler which may be the slow or quick drying type, depending on space and speed of schedule. It is applied in the regular manner and wiped from both veneer and gum parts in order to maintain a uniform color.

FIRST COATING

Overnight in the case of the slow, and within four hours in the case of the quick drying filler, a coat of lacquer sealer of good body is sprayed on, allowed to dry two hours and then sanded with 6/0 sandpaper.

SHADING

Rather as a color uniforming measure than for high-lighting purposes, a lacquer shading stain is now sprayed uniformly over the piece and allowed to dry for 30 minutes.

FINISH COATS

At this point the first of two finish coats of gloss rubbing lacquer is applied, followed by another in from two to four hours. This last coat is rubbed with 320 or 340 wet-or-dry sandpaper and polished.

DECORATION

Decoration is rare beyond matching of fancy veneers, and occasional two-toning.

CHAPTER V

BREAKFAST ROOM FURNITURE

THE increasing trend toward narrower dimensions in American homes, alike in city and suburbs, combined with the realization that economy in space is most readily effected in the dining room, has established a new type of furniture—the breakfast room or dinette style. Miniatured in proportions, the best examples express in design and finish daintiness, dignity and durability.

The brighter stained and painted styles are most popular for the country home—in the city the more subdued paint shades or the more sombre tones of stain are preferred. The variety of treatment in point of finish is so great that it will be best to cite the most common methods, the wood as always, playing an important part.

STAIN—WALNUT AND MAHOGANY

1.—A coat of water stain, high-lighted and shaded if desired, a wash coat of shellac, paste wood filler, shellac and two coats of rubbing varnish or clear body lacquer, rubbed dull. This system is preferred for mahogany; the wash coat and filler may be omitted if an antique open-pored walnut effect is preferred.

2.—A coat of non-grain-raising stain, wood filler, shading stain, lacquer sealer, a coat of flat lacquer.

3.—A coat of oil stain, shellac wash coat, wood filler, one coat varnish pigment coater or shellac substitute or 2 lb.-cut shellac, shading stain for high-lighted effect, one coat flat varnish. Gloss lacquer rubbed is preferable on table tops, but should not be

158

applied over shellac substitute nor should lacquer sealer and flat lacquer be used for a clear toned mahogany finish.

STAIN—BIRCH, GUM AND POPLAR

4.—Same as 1, 2 or 3, omitting shellac wash coat and wood filler.

STAIN—OAK

5.—Water stain, any shade of gray, brown, yellow, red, green or orchid, wash coat white shellac, white pigment wood filler, white shellac and wax or flat lacquer. It is impracticable to use varnish over gray stain as it may turn the color in the lighter shades an unsightly green as, for instance, with silver gray oak.

6.—Combination stain-filler in gray, brown or bright novelty colors, lacquer shading stain, one or more coats of flat lacquer, varnish or wax. If desired a pigment wiping stain may be applied and the work left unfilled for an antique flat lacquer finish.

7.—Lacquer enamel reduced one part to four or more of reducer, white or colored filler, one coat of pale gloss or flat lacquer. The above finishes may be enlivened by high lighting, two-toning with paint or a darker shade of stain, hand-painting, vein lining, transfers, imitation marquetry or striping. Oak in addition may be frosted, banded and stenciled.

PAINT—BASSWOOD, BIRCH, GUM AND POPLAR

Undercoaters should be carefully adapted to the nature of the wood. Thus, where soft woods like gum, basswood, magnolia and poplar are employed, the oil primer should be given an extra proportion of boiled oil to satisfy suction, but if the wood is hard like birch or maple, the addition of a little turpentine will increase penetration and insure a firmer anchorage.

Unless the wood is sanded to perfect smoothness and patched where necessary with white lead or lacquer putty, a flawlessly smooth finish is impossible. Moreover the better the grade of undercoater, *i.e.*, the more finely it is ground, the less necessity there will be for sanding and hence danger of cutting through nibs.

OIL ENAMEL

8.—Two coats oil undercoater, tinted to desired shade, followed by one coat eggshell enamel left natural or one coat gloss enamel, rubbed dull. Decorate over top coat with japan color

Breakfast table with walnut stain.

mixed in a little rubbing varnish to even up lustre. On coarser grained lumber an extra coat of enamel is often advisable.

PAINT UNDERCOATER AND VARNISH

9.—Three coats oil undercoater, tinted to desired shade, decorate and protect with one coat rubbing varnish rubbed dull or one coat flat varnish. The varnish will turn the lighter shades of undercoat color somewhat and this should be allowed for in selecting the shade. If desired the third primer coat may be eliminated in favor of a coat of white shellac as a base for decorations, or an extra shellac coat may be applied just prior

Breakfast chair with walnut stain.

to the varnish. Flat varnish is not so desirable on table tops as rubbing varnish.

PAINT UNDERCOATER AND CLEAR LACQUER

10.—Same as above except that gloss lacquer or flat lacquer is substituted for rubbing varnish and flat varnish. This is speedier, but the materials used in decorating as well as the undercoater itself must be of a nature rendering them adaptable for use under lacquer without softening.

JAPAN COLOR AND CLEAR LACQUER

11.—For a very speedy finish apply one coat japan color, decorate and finish with one coat lacquer sealer and gloss lacquer, rubbed dull, or one coat gloss lacquer and flat lacquer. The wood must be extremely smooth for a job of this nature.

LACQUER ENAMEL—BASSWOOD, BIRCH, GUM AND POPLAR

12.—One coat pigment lacquer undercoater, tinted one quart of colored lacquer enamel to the gallon, sanded and followed in four hours by lacquer enamel of desired shade. An extra coat of lacquer enamel may be applied for greater body, but in either case the top coat may be rubbed dull, polished or given a clear coat of flat lacquer over decorations to save rubbing or a clear coat of pale gloss lacquer rubbed dull or polished, for extra durability and resistance to wear.

TRANSPARENT LACQUER ENAMEL FINISH

13.—One coat lacquer enamel of desired shade, mixed one part to twelve or fifteen of clear gloss lacquer. Sand smooth in five hours, decorate and apply a second coat of clear lacquer, flat or gloss, to be rubbed dull. Walnut and mahogany stain effects may be procured by selecting nut brown and reddish brown shades, novelty color effects with bright greens and reds, the wood grain showing through in all cases. By regulating the spray mixture, antique and color shading may be introduced into the first coat or antique lacquer shading stain may be used over the reduced lacquer enamel as a separate operation.

CHAPTER VI

NOVELTY FURNITURE

NOVELTY furniture is a trade term comprising a class of semi-utilitarian, semi-decorative pieces of which the following are leading examples: End tables, humidors, cellarettes, Priscilla and Martha Washington sewing cabinets, book troughs, magazine carriers, book cases, hanging shelves, gate-leg, coffee, tilt-top and card tables, telephone sets (cabinet or table and chair), tabourets, consoles, corner and smaller secretary desks.

The fact that their dimensions are small makes it desirable to introduce color into the finish wherever possible, as decoratively they serve to enliven the general room scheme, standing out in relief against the more sombre tones of walnut and mahogany furniture. However, this is not always the case, since oftentimes this color note is sufficiently carried out in drapes and upholstery so that the finish color in the novelty pieces is intended rather to harmonize with, if not actually to match, the principal walnut and mahogany pieces.

STAIN

If for the latter purpose, the wood is stained, and filled if necessary, as outlined under *Radio Cabinets,* finished and decorated in the same manner. Gum, poplar and birch are the common woods with some walnut and mahogany veneer on the better grades.

PAINT AND LACQUER ENAMEL

Where the color note is to predominate, any of the systems mentioned under *Enameled Wood Furniture, Art Metal Furniture* and *Breakfast Room Furniture* may be employed, ac-

163

Mahogany wine stand.

cording to the wood or metal used in construction. It is noteworthy in this connection that an ever increasing amount of novelty furniture is being turned out in aluminum, steel and

Early American cherry candle stand.

malleable iron. Waste baskets are frequently of sheet steel grained.

COLOR SCHEMES

Appropriate colors for novelty furniture include Chinese red, jade green, lettuce green, Chinese yellow, turquoise blue, amber, parchment, French gray, gray green, cardinal red, lavender, champagne and black. All of these that harmonize may be used in combination.

In decoration novelty furniture may riot; in fact, practically every method outlined in Book I may be employed according

Carved mahogany piece.

as the piece may be stained, painted or lacquer enameled. Stain and paint are frequently combined, as on secretary desks, which may be of shaded maple, banded and striped in color, the interior finished in a bright glazed color to match banding or striping. The doors may be done in an oriental lacquered or hand-painted landscape scene.

Stencils and hand-painted floral and fruit groups are suitable for corner cabinets which may also be banded or striped and antiqued glazed. Much of the decoration of novelty furniture is coarse and crude in character; this is largely a fault of execution rather than a necessary economy in labor or materials. As a consequence delicately treated work stands out in superiority and commands a proportionately higher price at no greater cost.

Three legged cherry tilt top table.

CHAPTER VII

UPHOLSTERED FURNITURE

FOR obvious reasons the frames of upholstered furniture are finished prior to the upholstering. The wood used for the better grades is birch, for the cheaper grades, gum; if elaborately carved, oak, mahogany or walnut is employed. Practically all of the finish coats except shellac can be and often are dipped, although the brush and spray lend themselves better to special classes of work where the design is elaborate. A comparatively shallow tank will take care of all dipping require‹ ments nicely.

GUM

Gum frames are stained the desired shade with walnut or mahogany water stain, followed by shellac substitute, clear varnish firstcoater and flat varnish, lightly rubbed. For very cheap work oil stain may be substituted for water stain, but the gum should be of an even texture and as free as possible from sap streaks. Two coats shellac and wax is an alternative finish.

BIRCH AND MAPLE

Birch frames are stained with non-grain-raising or water stain and either; (1) two coats of shellac, sanded, and wax; or (2) shellac, clear coach and flat varnish; or (3) lacquer sealer and flat lacquer lightly rubbed; or (4) lacquer sealer and gloss lacquer, rubbed, or (5) a coat of clear gloss brushing lacquer, left natural.

OAK, WALNUT AND MAHOGANY

Open-pored woods may be finished the same as birch, except that paste wood filler is employed over the stain which should

169

also be wash coated with shellac. Very high-grade, hand-carved work is water stained and often french polished by hand.

DECORATION

Where pigment oil stain is used, as on unfilled antique oak, the raised parts of the frame may be high-lighted by wiping

Hand-carved mahogany chair.

while the stain is still wet, with water stain by steel wooling after it is dry. Spirit shading stain may be used to advantage by spraying over the shellac, sealer or filler coat provided the body stain color is not too dark.

On carved oak and walnut frames it is often the practice to antique dust in the recesses; frames of Spanish or Italian design are frequently polychromed in gold, red, blue and green.

Mahogany frame chair.

CHAPTER VIII

A PART from the special types considered elsewhere in this book, enameled furniture includes bedroom and living room suites, the finish for which will be described first, and bathroom and juvenile pieces. The choice of the method for the former depends largely on the grade and style, the woods being chiefly birch and gum, although mahogany, oak and walnut may also be used provided they are first surfaced with paste wood filler and shellac wash coated.

PAINT AND VARNISH

On lower-priced work of gum a sealer wash coat of shellac or shellac substitute is first applied, sanded in three or four hours, puttied where necessary with white lead-varnish putty and given one coat flat paint undercoater, finely ground so as to require only a light sanding in eighteen hours. Decorations consisting of shading, stipple glazing or decalcomania transfers are then applied, followed by one coat flat varnish to avoid rubbing. For better grade popular furniture an extra coat of paint undercoater may be substituted for the shellac sealer coat and rubbing varnish substituted for flat varnish. It would also be possible to mask off and two-tone on frame, drawer fronts or overlays and add banding or striping to decorations, using a different shade of flat enamel for the former and japan color for the latter.

PAINT AND LACQUER

On high grade work, usually birch, two coats of paint under-coater, each carefully sanded, are followed by shading, then

172

decoration consisting of striping and hand-painting.   If desired to spray stipple or shade as well, a coat of 3 lb.-cut white shellac is applied, sanded smooth, followed by two coats of pale body lacquer, both sprayed on the same day, but the second al-

Modern directors chair in white enamel.

lowed to stand three days before rubbing.   Flat lacquer may be used as second lacquer coat to save rubbing.

LACQUER ENAMEL

A coat of lacquer clear first coater is first sprayed on, tinted with some of the body lacquer, followed by one or two full wet coats of lacquer enamel. Stripes, hand-painting or transfer decorations are next applied, protected with clear flat lacquer or gloss lacquer to be rubbed down. Here again it is possible to two-tone by masking off, to decorate parts of the piece with

Enameled stadium seat.

glaze stippling or crackle lacquer, banding with brushing lacquer enamel, or to omit clear lacquer coat.

COLOR SCHEMES

Favorite colors for such furniture include principally the pastel shades and should be selected with care: Fawn, pale blue, pea green, lettuce green, parchment, French and putty gray, ivory, cream and mauve. In the stronger tones Chinese red, jade green and ebony black predominate. All but black may be shaded antique or in a deeper tone of the body color, but with the utmost delicacy or the work is ruined. Black is best banded, striped or lightly shaded with gold bronze. Varnish,

Enameled childrens room desk.

and to a lesser extent lacquer, will affect the light colors when applied as a top coat and this should be allowed for.

JUVENILE FURNITURE

Furniture for the children include beds, bassinets, high and low chairs, desks, tables, breakfast sets, etc. Very little of this represents any attempt at real quality in finish, owing to the fact that it stands unusual abuse and is discarded with advancing age. Ordinarily one or two coats of white or tinted paint undercoater, direct on the wood or over shellac substitute wash coats, are followed by a coat of tough oil gloss enamel, left in the natural high lustre or rubbed on higher grade work. Lacquer enamel may be used over clear firstcoater where the selling price permits.

Two-toning, banding, striping, or stencils and transfers on overlays are applied to the top coat and left unprotected, but in darker shades they are put on the flat undercoater and finished over with clear gloss varnish, unrubbed. Much of this work, which is plain in design, can be finished by dipping; cane is finished natural or in the same enamel color as the body, namely, ivory, pink or pale blue.

BATHROOM AND KITCHEN FURNITURE

Bathroom stools and hampers and kitchen stools, chairs and tables are given one or two dip coats of heavy-bodied, good hiding flat white paint undercoater with only light sanding, followed by one dip coat of high gloss white oil or lacquer enamel left in the natural lustre. Owing to the mixed nature of the woods used in construction which may be of soft or hard fibre the undercoater should be selected with great care so that it will satisfy the suction of the porous pieces. Decoration is confined to banding in a deep blue shade of enamel on kitchen furniture.

Since the world war greater color variety has been introduced alike into the bathroom and kitchen furniture. This is due to the fact that both rooms are being given more and more of a decorative treatment in curtains, wall colors and wallpaper patterns. Plain white does not harmonize with these, so that greens, blues and warm grays have become the vogue in order to carry out the scheme fully.

Metal bathroom or kitchen furniture is enameled as outlined under *Refrigerators and Kitchen Cabinets*, the former by dipping.

CHAPTER IX

SCHOOL FURNITURE

IN recent years extensive research in the field of eyestrain has determined that correct seeing conditions in a classroom depend not only on the type of natural or artificial light available but on the light distribution characteristics of all the surfaces in the room. In this respect the dark finishes applied to school desks and seats in pre-war days were major offenders since they offered a light reflection value of but 15 per cent for the wood portions and less than half of that for the enameled metal parts.

Why, then, not do away with stain altogether and go to a natural finish? The practical objection is that it is impossible to obtain sufficient clear birch, maple or beech to accomplish this whereas the vast supply of these woods in unselected grades would show up in unsightly striped effects when so finished.

A MODERN SCHEDULE

The problem therefore calls for a compromise whereby the wood is first stained with a non-grain-raising stain in a honey maple shade known as "Sun-Tan." This dries in about 4 hours, unifies any uneven color inherent in the wood and is still more light reflectant than the old walnut shades.

The next operation calls for a sealer coat of an alkyd resin type lacquer, one of which is known as "Celsyn." This must be sprayed as received and allowed to dry overnight or force dried in 5 to 6 hours and then lightly sanded with 6/0 paper.

The finish coat calls for a coat of the same material, also unreduced and allowed to dry in the same manner. The resultant sheen is a semi-gloss much superior to a glare producing high gloss finish and the whole will show a light reflectance value of

177

Courtesy of Peabody Seating Co.

School desk and seat of maple.

Assembly room seats of birch.

35 per cent. This finish, incidentally, is also in a very high degree mar proof.

For the metal standards a Sun-Tan or Neutral Gray baked enamel should be used which will give these portions of the desk or seat a light reflectance value of 20 per cent.

SEATS

Assembly and auditorium chairs of birch and maple are water stained a light brown or finished natural with two coats chair dipping coach varnish, the first slightly thinned with naphtha. The metal sides are of mixed iron and steel finished in baking enamel in optional shades.

CHAPTER X

OUTDOOR FURNITURE

OUTDOOR furniture comprises principally porch chairs, settees, swings and tables, also lawn chairs, benches and swings, and camp furniture. The finish, of course, depends on the construction, wood or metal, and whether the former is to be natural or painted. Durability, it goes without saying, is the prime requisite with all.

WOOD

Natural.—Where oak, birch or maple are to be given a natural finish, the procedure is to apply one or two coats of good waterproof coach varnish, similar to that used on refrigerators, but not quite so high in quality. In the case of oak, the wood is first filled on better grades with a paste wood filler of the shade known as natural, which is colorless. Birch and maple require no paste filler, but are frequently given a coat of clear varnish firstcoater. Filler, firstcoater and varnish are customarily dipped and tipped off with a brush except where the shape of the object precludes free draining, in which case they are sprayed. Backs, sides and seats of porch swings are dipped separately and then assembled when finished and dry.

Stain.—On some types of outdoor furniture, particularly for the porch, the wood is first stained prior to filling or firstcoating. Except forest green, which requires a water stain, oil stain is satisfactory and shows up clear in tone on the hardwoods mentioned. Antique and fumed oak are the favorite colors, applied by dipping and sealed with shellac instead of a varnish firstcoater. For a mission effect omit filler from oak and finish with flat varnish over firstcoater. The forest green

180

water stain is ordinarily applied to maple which is so hard in texture that the grain is raised but little, requiring practically no sanding.

Enamel.—Outdoor porch furniture is usually painted a solid color, vermillion red or medium chrome green. The wood is birch or Oregon pine, the first coat flat paint primer tinted red or green, the finish coat high-gloss tough enamel or color varnish, specially constructed to resist water and wear. For a higher grade job one or two coats of flat paint primer are followed by striping, protected with a coat of clear waterproof

Porch bench in flat black enamel.

coach varnish. All outdoor furniture varnishes are left in the natural gloss with little or no sanding on the first coat since an absolutely smooth job is not essential.

Outdoor lawn furniture is usually built of cypress and finished in white in two grades as follows: (1) Two thin coats white lead and oil, thinned with plenty of turpentine, followed by one or two coats lead and zinc outside white house paint, the first thin, all coats brushed and without sanding between coats; (2) two thin coats finely ground paint undercoater, to the first of which is added a proportion of benzole to increase penetration, a third of the same slightly heavier, all sanded smooth, followed by one or two coats first grade long-oil gloss enamel. Both of these finishing systems are necessarily slow as paints on cypress are slow drying—thick undercoats heavy in oil often scale. Cypress, while noted for its resistance to decay,

Redwood picnic table.

also contains an oily sap which feels waxy to the touch; to remove or neutralize this for painting, a preliminary wash with benzine is desirable, adding benzole to the first coat in addition, as above mentioned. All end wood should be sealed with paste white lead so as to prevent penetration of moisture at these vulnerable points, especially on legs.

METAL

Metal outdoor furniture whether sheet, cane or tubular, is finished with one coat of zinc chromate rust-inhibitive baking primer, followed by one coat high gloss synthetic baking enamel, white or colors.

Metal serving cart.

Metal patio chair.

CHAPTER XI
OFFICE FURNITURE

OFFICE furniture in the main is constructed of oak, walnut or mahogany and comprises desks, chairs, filing cases, hat trees, tables and benches.

Oak is usually first filled with paste filler or combination stain and filler in paste form, shellaced and given one coat each varnish pigment first coater and flat varnish or lacquer sealer and flat lacquer. The shade of the filler is natural or a very light golden color.

Mahogany and walnut office furniture.

Walnut is customarily stained a medium light shade with oil or water stain, followed by a coat of thin shellac, brown or transparent black wood filler, body shellac and two coats rubbing varnish or lacquer sealer and gloss or flat lacquer.

Mahogany is water stained a colonial red color, such as obtained by mixing two ounces standard mahogany red with four ounces standard mahogany brown aniline powder in one gallon water; a water stain is essential as an oil or spirit stain would quickly fade under the strong light to which office furniture is subjected. The stain is followed by a wash coat of shellac, a red or transparent black paste wood filler, a body shellac coat and two coats rubbing varnish or gloss rubbing lacquer.

Matched oak conference table.

Hat trees, chairs and benches are often finished with two dip coats waterproof coach varnish over the shellac, lightly sanding the first but leaving the second in gloss. Desk panels and filing case parts may also be dipped separately and assembled only when ready for the final varnish or lacquer coat. On desk sides flat lacquer over sealer or flat varnish over coach is satisfactory.

CHAPTER XII

CHAIRS

THE question of the best finish method for chairs is almost as large as the number of types and designs of chairs. Where made to form a part of dining and bedroom suites, they are finished and decorated to match; for living room purposes they can show all the originality of finish found in novelty and period furniture; for strictly utilitarian purposes, like restaurant, porch and office pieces, they are finished along production lines.

DINING AND LIVING ROOM CHAIRS

Most "suite" chairs, exclusive of upholstered pieces, are of gum or birch with occasional veneers, overlays and inlays of rarer woods. They must be carefully matched in color, shading, striping, glazing, two-toning, etc., to the suite of which they are to form a part.

Living room chairs are apt to be of period design, upholstered or caned. Some types can be finished by dipping, but most require to be sprayed, including painted designs.

UTILITY CHAIRS

On bentwood and other utilitarian chairs a water stain is impracticable, owing to the expense of sanding down the raised fibres, and it is impossible to make a combination water stain and filler. About the cheapest way to finish a chair made of birch, beech or elm, or all three mixed in indiscriminately, as is often the case, is to dip it in asphaltum varnish thinned one part to three of solvent naphtha, followed by one dip or spray coat of cheap coach varnish. This will give a fair golden oak shade and offer a reasonable resistance to wear, for the price. By thinning

187

the asphaltum varnish somewhat less, the shade of the finish may be made to approach that of walnut.

Early American captain's chair.

Auditorium, assembly room and folding chairs of maple are finished natural with two dip coats of water and printproof coach varnish, neither sanded or rubbed. For a mahogany finish birch is used, first stained with mahogany water stain, then shellaced, sanded, given one coat varnish firstcoater and finished with one coat flat varnish. All coats are dipped and drained on a rack using a brush only to catch and tip off the drip at the lowest point.

ENAMEL CHAIRS

Utility enamel chairs for kitchens and restaurants can be turned out presentably with a first coat of cheap paint undercoater, not much finer than the flat paint used on plastered walls, and one coat quick-drying gloss oil enamel. The wood for such chairs is usually a combination of glued sections of hard and soft woods, with the result that the average primer will not have enough thinner to penetrate the former nor enough oil to satisfy the latter.

Children's high chair of birch.

CHURCH PEWS

Church and lodge furniture may be stained and filled in the regular manner, but a special varnish or lacquer must be employed which will not print or stick in humid weather, or turn white on contact with water. Pew varnish is a special high gloss article meeting these specifications, and is readily obtainable.

CHAPTER XIII

DRAWERS AND INTERIORS

THE woods commonly used in drawer and interior construction are such close-pored woods as birch, beech, sycamore and basswood, with cypress and pine for sides. Walnut, cedar and mahogany are used in high grade furniture, sometimes alone, sometimes for drawer bottoms in combination with red gum or one or another of the harder woods above mentioned for the sides. The first essential of a good drawer finish is to seal the wood and render it possible for the housekeeper to dust and clean it readily without in time producing a splotched or dingy interior. It must also be waterproof and free of coloring matter which might come off on clothing. From a production viewpoint it must also be economical in cost, not too difficult to apply and if possible of a tone harmonizing with the exterior stain color.

CLOSE-PORED WOODS

1. *Shellac.*—One coat of the pure orange article, three to four and one-half pound cut, drys quickly, fills well and gives a fairly agreeable natural lustre without rubbing. However it mars readily on contact with moisture.

2. *Shellac Substitute.*—Usually cheaper than the above and popular chiefly for this reason. A few are waterproof, but most are not; when tinted with alcohol soluble anilines the color will fade and possibly come off on contact with moisture, as spirit colors are partially soluble in water.

3. *Wax.*—Over one coat of shellac or substitute, wax offers a surface easy to keep clean and more agreeable in lustre than either of the above. The wax may be tinted.

4. *Wax.*—Used alone it is a purely temporary proposition. When tinted with color in oil, heat or contact with anything

190

greasy or oily may soften it and cause the color to come off.
If wax alone is applied, the wood must be sanded extra smooth.

Use of wax to help drawer to move easily.

5. *Varnish Leavings.*—A slush coat may be made by working
over the drippings and skins of varnish with benzine that will
answer as a finish on very cheap work.   Unless the mixture is
well strained it gives a coarse finish with an uneven gloss.   An
economy job pure and simple best suited to backs.

6. *Flat Varnish.*—Very popular for the better class of furni-

ture, usually applied over a first coat of shellac, substitute, or varnish firstcoater. Possesses much of the merit of wax with none of the drawbacks, though naturally more expensive in cost and slower in drying than any of the above.

7. *Oil.*—This method operates as follows: Apply two thin coats of shellac or substitute; sand and oil off with a rag saturated in paraffin oil. This is quick and inexpensive and gives an agreeable lustre, but is not durable and may be affected by heat.

8. *Drawer Coater.*—There are a number of leading brands most of which are based on one or another of the above. They are waterproof, may be obtained tinted, and vary in cost and speed of drying according to whether on a shellac, substitute or varnish base.

9. *Coach Varnish.*—May be obtained at low cost and makes an excellent undercoat for wax or flat varnish, but alone is not recommended on porous softwoods and does not give an agreeable lustre. It is sometimes tinted a light oak or walnut shade by adding a little asphaltum varnish. One objection, which also applies to varnish leavings, is that hot weather may tend to make it sticky.

10. *Rubbing Varnish.*—When employed as a drawer finish only a light rub is given—just enough to knock off the gloss. An undercoat is required as for flat varnish; for a tinted effect the wood must first be stained or wiped over with filler. This is distinctly a quality method for quality furniture.

11. *Lacquer.*—Excellent over filler on open-pored woods and is waterproof, quick drying and tight sealing, but used alone lacks body and filling qualities and possesses an odor that lingers in closed interiors. Lacquer may be tinted in all wood shades with spirit soluble anilines and at least two coats should be applied, the first lacquer or lacquer sealer, the second flat lacquer for its agreeable lustre.

OPEN-PORED WOODS AND CEDAR

These may be finished the same as above except that paste wood filler of desired shade is required first. Where filler is used no stain need be applied even on high class work as it imparts sufficient coloring in being wiped off. Liquid filler will often serve for thin "wash" veneers on bottoms. Aromatic cedar should be left unfinished.

COLORING

On cheaper work an orange tone as found in shellac or the amber tone of substitute or varnish is sufficient, except possibly in the case of very white woods like birch. Where stain is used it should be reduced many shades lighter than the exterior, but should harmonize in tone; thinned paste wood filler may be wiped on the wood and then quickly wiped off to give a semi-stained effect at low cost.

APPLICATION

A well sanded drawer or interior is already half finished. If stained or filled the drawer bottoms may be dipped, dried and then assembled to be finished by spraying. All but lacquer and some substitute shellacs may be successfully applied by brushing as well as spraying and very cheap work can be dipped in varnish, reduced very thin. Varnish on work of any quality, however, should never be applied to the outside edges of drawers as it becomes gummy with heat and causes the drawer to stick. Wax is best for all points of contact between drawer and frame.

CHAPTER XIV

PICTURE frame mouldings come for the most part in long strips already machined or pressed out in a running design by heat. As the woods employed, mostly gum with some bass, are rather soft, the mouldings sometimes reach the finisher already filled to smoothness with white glue primer, as for bathroom mirror frames; if not it is customary to procure a special sealer-surfacer of whiting and glue, to be colored a brick red, for burnishing applied by brush or spray and sanded smooth. Over this there is sprayed a base color coat of bronze powder, pale, rich or Roman gold, mixed in water and glue. Fine lining bronzes are essential for this work, especially as it is customary to burnish the high lights with the agate tool made for the purpose. The whole is then antique or color glazed over a sealer coat of clear lacquer or shellac. Or the moulding may be polychromed, according to whether the design is already pressed in the wood, placed there by raised stippling or else flat stippled. A coat of thin pale lacquer is usually applied over all polychroming for protective purposes. On cheaper frames iridescent Tiffany polychrome effects are procured with distemper colors mixed in a good grade of glue. This dries quickly and requires no clear protective top coating, unless a gloss finish is desired.

Metal leaf may also be applied to the fine grades of picture frames, the gold size, usually japan, being applied over the primer-sealer. Dutch silver leaf (Schlagmetal) may be applied at much less expense than the gold leaf and given a gold appearance by spraying on a coat of gold toning lacquer. It will not tarnish, but should be lightly wiped with beeswax; it should not be burnished.

194

Imitation leather effects may be procured by spraying a coat of clear lacquer over the primer, followed by black crackle lacquer, then brown lacquer enamel and antique glazing if desired.

Carved mahogany mirror with metal leaf.

All sorts of novelty effects are possible—the list is limited only by the selling price and the willingness of the operator to experiment.

CHAPTER XV

MODERN WOOD FINISH SYSTEMS

U NDER this heading are grouped those various finish effects which have come into vogue since the first edition of this book was published. All of them have been widely used and often appear, with slight variations in color and process of finishing, under other names, as when bestowed by individual manufacturers or studios for christening purposes.

BONE WHITE

This finish is also known variously as Egyptian White, Old Bone, and Antique White. It is most popular on novelty furniture, bedroom suites, dinettes, and odd chairs, usually in a semi-classic design. Some of the woods commonly used are gum, basswood or poplar, or unfilled walnut for a pronounced effect.

First Coat.—This may be one coat of either sanding lacquer sealer or pure white flat drying lacquer enamel, either one sanded with 6/0 paper after being allowed to dry for four hours.

Second Coat.—This is essential for the softer woods and consists of a white flat drying lacquer enamel, sanded as for the first coat.

Glaze Coat.—This consists of a mixture of equal parts oil and japan colors, using either raw umber alone, or additions of raw sienna and burnt umber. This is sprayed or brushed on and immediately wiped with soft cloths, then brushed with a badger hair blender on flat surfaces.

Finish Coat.—This should preferably be a water white flat lacquer to avoid a greenish effect, applied by spray after overnight drying of the glaze.

196

A variation from the conventional Bone White finishing practice calls for bleaching the darker woods, sanding with No. 1 or 2/0 steel wool, and applying a coat of water white sealer mixed in proportions of one quart sealer to 2 oz. white lacquer enamel. Glaze and finish coats are the same as previously given.

Mahogany boat rudder turned into a coffee table.

OLD WORLD FINISH

This is also known as Mellow Mahogany, Old English Mahogany and Georgian Mahogany, and is commonly used on Chippendale and Colonial designs. The object being to produce the original mellow color of 18th century originals, the stain is a very light shade of reddish brown, obtainable in non-grain-raising stains from wood finishing supply houses, or by mixing water stain powders in the ratio of 2 oz. mahogany brown and 1 oz. red to the gallon of water.

The latter is sprayed on, given two hours to dry, and then wash coated with shellac (one part to six parts alcohol). This is lightly sanded and followed with a filler of like shade, reduced four lbs. to one gallon benzine for a semi-open-pored

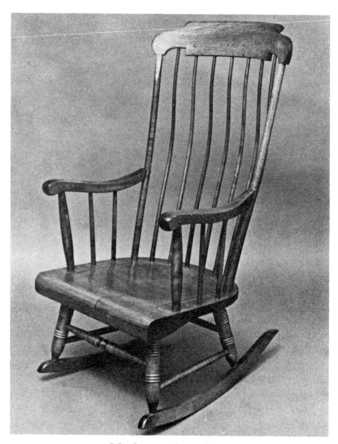

Modern oak rocker.

effect. When dry, a coat of shellac (two lb. cut) is sprayed all over and sanded.

The glaze coat follows and consists of Van Dyke Brown in japan heavily reduced with equal parts boiled oil and turpentine, the mixture brushed on all over with a common wall brush, and wiped with a soft cloth at the same time high-lighted on panel centers and raised parts of carvings. This wiping stain may also be obtained ready made, as Old World Wiping Glaze.

The finish, after overnight drying of the glaze, consists of shellac and a coat of flat lacquer.

Old English Walnut receives the same treatment, using a light colored stain and a filler to match, mixed five or six lbs. to the gallon of benzine to give a similar semi-open-pored effect.

MAPLE FINISHES

The variations of color and effect under this heading are legion; but fortunately the proper stains can be secured readily, and therefore only a few of the best known are described.

Vermont Maple is a taffy or honey color carried out in one operation with pigment wiping stain, or by first using non-grain-raising stain, and then a glaze made of equal parts raw and burnt sienna in both japan and oil, or purchased ready made. This is wiped and blended, then high lighted and finished with two coats of gloss lacquer rubbed, or one coat sealer and one of flat.

Cherry Maple calls for a redder stain, burnt sienna if pigment, followed by a glaze of chrome yellow and cadmium red.

Pilgrim Maple is on the brown side as to stain, and the glaze is a mixture of burnt umber with a trace of Van Dyke brown.

Blonde Maple in a natural or cream tone calls simply for a blonde lacquer sealer (which is slightly pigmented) and a finish coat of water white flat or gloss lacquer, rubbed and polished. For a lighter or platinum effect, the wood should first be given a bleaching.

BLEACHED EFFECTS

On modern designs the bleaching operation is called for on many woods other than maple, but for all of this work the two solution type described in Book I under "Matched Veneers" is preferred. In the case of *Maple*, both solid wood and veneers should be selected with the utmost care in order to avoid mineral streaks which remain unaffected by the bleach. When unavoidably encountered, such streaks must be fogged over with lacquer enamel or grained in by hand, if a very dark streak requires heavy application.

Although *Walnut* is darker than maple, less bleach should be used on this wood, since it may go through the veneer and attack the glue, thus forming gas bubbles which work up through the finish. Walnut stumpwood, being especially dark, requires care, since it is often necessary to repeat the bleaching up to four or five times with the No. 2 solution. Since natural filler may later turn gray in the pores, it is best to add a little color to it.

Mahogany, if not too red, may be finished in a bleached effect by finishing natural, i.e., wash coating with shellac and filling with natural filler, followed by water white lacquer. If the mahogany is very red it may be bleached sufficiently by a reduction with one part distilled water to two parts of the bleach as mixed.

All fuzz raised by the bleach should be sanded down and the surface given a spray coat of bleaching lacquer. This is slightly pigmented and helps to uniform and preserve the bleached effect at the same time as sealing the wood or veneer against subsequent lacquer coatings. The finish coats must be specially made water white lacquers, obtainable in all sheens, and since to keep them pale only a small amount of body is present, it is often necessary to apply two or three coats for a full bodied finish.

Pine is given a wash coat of one part each White Lacquer Enamel, Sealer and Reducer, followed by an Antique Oil Glaze, a coat of sealer, a coat of flat lacquer and a dusting with rotten stone over wax.

STAINED EFFECTS

Since the color or figure of the face veneer constitutes the chief, if not sole, decorative interest on much furniture of Modern design, it will be seen that the prime purpose of the finish is to enhance the beauty of the wood as unobtrusively as possible. Nevertheless, when a combination of veneers, such as satinwood, curly maple, orientalwood, American walnut, and tulipwood, all appear in a single piece, they may be individually treated as follows: The *satinwood* and *curly maple* is given a brush coat of silver gray water stain which somewhat lightens the golden color of the former and gives a grayish green glow to the latter. The *orientalwood* is given a coat of asphaltum walnut stain. A coat of lacquer sanding sealer is sprayed over the entire piece and sanded in a half hour with 3/0 paper. On the *satinwood* and *maple* veneers a white filler is used, on American walnut, orientalwood, and tulipwood, a light brown filler. A coat of lacquer sealer and two coats of gloss lacquer, rubbed and polished, complete the finish.

Where walnut, usually pencil stripe, is not bleached, it is ordinarily stained in weak amber tones. A typical water stain formula would be, to the gallon of water, four oz. orange, one oz. jet nigrosene, one oz. yellow. For an ebony effect one gum trim, the stain would be one oz. jet nigrosine to one gallon of alcohol, with four oz. shellac added for binder, and four oz. acetone for penetration.

PICKLED FINISH

This is applied to French Provincial or similar Antique designs of walnut, mahogany, oak or pine. In the case of mahogany a typical finish would call for a double bleach, a wash coat of white shellac, a natural or slightly tinted filler and an antique glaze. Pickled knotty pine requires a wash coat of white shellac, a light amber non-grain-raising stain and over the lacquer finish an application of rotten stone to catch in knots and crevices. The finish on all consists of a coat of sanding sealer, and one or two of flat lacquer.

FRUITWOOD FINISH

This is applied mostly to breakfast room furniture of such woods as maple, birch, gum or poplar, in Biedermeier designs,

and consists of a fruitwood lacquer, in tones of tan with a hint
of orange. Over one coat of this, a glaze of japan-oil color is

Pine sewing basket with maple stain.

applied, equal parts burnt umber and burnt sienna, wiped and
blended. The finish is flat lacquer over a coat of lacquer sealer,
and decoration is carried out over the sealer coat.

HAREWOOD FINISH

This name is applied to imitations of the genuine English Harewood, which is English "Sycamore" veneer dyed to a light gray color by a special process in which the veneer is stained all the way through after being cut. The imitation calls for curly maple veneer, stained very lightly with a solution of three to five grains of blue-black nigrosene to a gallon of water, followed after sanding by two or three coats of water white lacquer. The finish is used on some modern designs, also on Adam reproductions decorated in the Angelica Kauffman manner.

MODERN GLAZED FINISHES

While most of the glaze colors are manufactured on specification of furniture manufacturers, it is possible to imitate them with a mixture of equal parts of oil and japan colors, thinned with VMP naphtha to brushing or spraying consistency, depending on the method of application. This can be used for all maple finishes and the best method would be as follows:

Presuming this is to be over birch or maple wood as is the rule, it is desirable to spray over a ground color of non-grain-raising stain or a pigment wiping stain. The former is preferable because of the penetration into the wood and lends better to the glaze coating to be used later. For a honey maple finish characteristic of the Early American, you would use a golden oak shade of non-grain-raising stain sprayed at low pressure.

For a harvest or wheat finish, use a dull shade of yellow in the same manner.

For the cherry maple you would use an orange stain of the same type.

Spray over all these, a coat of clear lacquer sanding sealer and sand.

EARLY AMERICAN MAPLE FINISH

Mix a shade of glaze to match the stain used in color-testing, thin to spraying or brushing consistency, using equal parts of raw and burnt sienna, half oil colors and half japan as advised previously. Wipe good with soft rags and blend with a camel hair blender, high lighting the centers of panels with closer wiping.

The best finish for this is two coats of high grade gloss lacquer and rubbed to a satin finish.

CHERRY MAPLE FINISH

Spray over a stain of the color of chrysoidine yellow which is a bright red orange color. This can be mixed from two standard colors in the non-grain-raising stain namely orange and scarlet. One coat of clear lacquer sanding sealer and a glaze of chrome yellow medium, half and half with japan and oil colors, and thinned to working consistency. The usual wiping with soft rags, blending if desired and two gloss lacquer coats.

WHEAT FINISH

Yellow ochre represents about the nearest color to this finish, but, of course, may need some brown or a trace of yellow to make the proper glaze. The stain would be better made on the pigment base instead of aniline. The same procedure otherwise used on the preceding finishes.

Essentially the wheat finish was originally created on bleached mahogany veneers, but now a version of this can be found on birch, maple, or even beech.

The best type of this furniture is bleached mahogany or veneers, and best created by the use of a pigment wiping stain on the ochre shade followed by filler of same or slightly darker, followed by lacquer sealer coat, glaze of golden ochre, Vandyke brown and sometimes a trace of drop black thinned as advised for all glazes, two coats of gloss lacquer and dull rubbed.

When birch or maple is used to create this type of finish, a little varnish should be added to the stain for adhesion. The stain can be pigment wiping stain which lends itself to this type of finish as no aniline can be found to give this effect. One coat lacquer sanding sealer, glaze and one or two coats of gloss lacquer rubbed to satin finish.

On lower cost furniture of this finish you can eliminate the last gloss lacquer coat and substitute a dull rubbed effect lacquer.

Using any dark woods would require bleaching to get any reasonably good results and the costs would suggest using only light woods.

It is possible to adapt the finish to economical production methods by employing pigmented lacquers thus eliminating any necessity for bleaching out discolorations and sap streaks as would be necessary where stains are used. Lacquer shading pastes are obtainable in all colors making a great variety of color effects possible which are both fast to light and highly resistant to wear.

The first step is to open up the wood pores by working along the grain with a stiff bristle or wire brush. Follow this with sanding and finish by blowing all dust out of the pores in order to leave them perfectly clean.

The lacquer enamel used for the ground or color coat is readily obtainable or may be purchased in white and tinted by adding one or more of the above mentioned shading pastes. It is also possible to buy these color coats ready to spray from any lacquer house. The reducer used should be of the slow type in order to permit the color coat to sink readily into the pores and make the effect transparent. An average mixture would be one part lacquer enamel to three or four parts lacquer reducer or one part enamel to two parts reducer and two parts clear lacquer.

After the color coat has dried several hours it may be sanded lightly with fine paper and is then ready for filling. This is accomplished in the normal manner by reducing eight to ten pounds of paste wood filler with a gallon of naphtha, brushing or spraying it on and allowing it to "flash off," i.e., go flat. This usually requires 10 to 15 minutes after which it is padded in and all surplus cleaned off *across* the grain. The filler, incidentally, should not be of coarse quality or it may scour the color coat when wiped off.

When the filler has dried, usually overnight, the finish coats may be applied. These normally consist of a lacquer sealer and a gloss, semi-gloss or flat clear lacquer, the paler the better .

The color coat for Lime Oak varies from a light amber to a light burned oak color and for British Oak a natural clear lacquer with merely a trace of amber shading paste, if any. Green Lime Oak carries a trace of green in the color coat and Gray Oak similarly black. In all cases the filler is white.

Equally interesting effects are obtained with a white color coat and a dark gray or green filler, a light tan color coat and a light reddish brown filler. The possible variations in harmonizing or contrasting color coat-filler combinations are, of course, limited only by the finisher's imagination.

PLATINUM MAHOGANY FINISH

This is a name of convenience applied to Blond or Bleached effects on mahogany veneers of furniture in modern designs on which it is desired to retain only the characteristic figured markings without the natural pinkish color peculiar to the wood. For a true platinum effect two applications are made of the bleach.

Care must be taken to insure the absolute dryness of the bleached surface prior to application of the sealer in order to avoid later difficulties with "bubbling." While a drying kiln will speed up the bleach's normal overnight drying such forced drying will also detract from the bleaching power. The more time allowed the bleach to dry the better will be its penetration and consequently its effectiveness.

Where a double bleach is applied it is also well to apply a neutralizing solution after the bleached surfaces are thoroughly dried and sanded. This solution may consist of equal parts white vinegar and distilled water or a small amount of acetic acid added to water. This procedure is an added help in meeting the problem of blisters or bubbles so common in bleached finishes even though it requires added drying time before proceeding.

The next steps call for (1) a wash coat of white shellac or lacquer sealer, (2) sanding, (3) an application of a filler consisting of equal parts natural and white and (4) the conventional protective coats of the palest obtainable gloss or semigloss lacquers. Alternately a bleach diluted with distilled water, one part to two of the mixed bleach, and a natural filler tinted with a little Raw Sienna and a trace of Burnt Sienna may be employed to produce the so-called Sun-Tan mahogany effect.

BLEACHED WALNUT

The bleaching of walnut represents a particular problem in that veneers frequently contain dark streaks which will show up brown or black even after a double bleach. One bleach is therefore advisable, relying on hand tinting of any prominent dark streaks with pigmented touch-up lacquer to subdue them.

After wash coating, the same filler is applied as recommended for Sun-Tan Mahogany followed by orange shellac or an amber toned lacquer sealer. After this has dried and been sanded an antique glaze is applied consisting of two parts Burnt Umber to one part Raw Sienna ground in japan and reduced with turpentine.

The glaze may be brushed or sprayed on with particular attention to blending out on flat surfaces and wiping on the high points of carvings and mouldings in order to produce an aged effect. This, when dry, is protected with same orange or amber sealer previously employed and the whole finished with flat lacquer.

Bleached Walnut finishes as above described are particularly favored for French Provincial designs.

CHAPTER XVI

MIRROR RESILVERING

THE equipment necessary for mirror silvering consists of an inclined washing rack, a movable table on casters and a large solidly-made silvering table. This last is covered with canvas stretched tight over a layer of felt so as to give a firm surface which at the same time will yield enough to prevent breakage of the glass. Underneath the table top, and about equal to it in size, is placed a shallow metal tank, full of water, through which a system of steam pipes is passed back and forth to be kept at a uniform heat.

Removing the Old Backing.—The initial operation calls for removing the old paint and silver, the first with paint and varnish remover, the second with nitric acid or a mixture of nitric and sulphuric acid. The latter is rubbed on gently with a ball of cotton batting tied around the end of a stick dipped into the acid. It is then mounted on the wash rack and washed clean with distilled water, after which it is ready for the application of the tin solution.

The Tin Solution.—Now mix a solution composed of one ounce of muriate of tin (crystals) to one gallon of distilled water and pour on over the glass. When it has drained down over the entire glass,. pour on clear distilled water; it will appear to wash off the tin solution, but actually a sufficient trace will be left. The glass is then moved from the rack to the heated silvering table so that in the next operation it will be warm enough for the silver nitrate solution to precipitate. It is desirable to place small V-shaped wedges under the edges of the mirror in order first, to assure its being exactly level, and secondly, to make the mirror easier to lift off when the silvering has been completed.

The Sliver Nitrate Solution.—The next step is to apply the silvering solution, which is composed of two solutions prepared separately, then mixed together in equal parts. All of the chemicals can be secured from a druggist who, on request, will also do the weighing.

A Solution.—Dissolve 120 grains of silver nitrate in two fluid ounces of distilled water and pour quickly into a boiling solution of 96 grains rochelle salts mixed in two fluid ounces distilled water. When cool filter through filtering paper into a glass jar, or bottle and make up to twenty-four fluid ounces with distilled water.

B Solution.—Dissolve 120 grains of silver nitrate in two fluid ounces of distilled water and add ammonia until the precipitation is nearly completed. Then make up to twenty-four fluid ounces with distilled water and filter into glass container as above described.

Silvering.—When the two solutions have been mixed into one, it is poured slowly on the glass so as to cover completely without running off. After being left on the silvering table fifteen to twenty minutes, the mirror will have gradually taken on a uniformly grayish appearance which indicates complete precipitation of the silver. The mirror is now gently tipped to permit the free top layer of water to run off onto the canvas, after which it is carefully placed on the movable table and gently tapped with a chamois skin to remove all remaining moisture.

Painting.—When the mirror is completely dry, a coat of thin shellac is applied over the silvering as it has been found that this gives a good foundation for the paint and adds to life of the silver. When this is dry a coat of special mirror backing paint is brushed on. This paint comes in paste form in various shades of gray to be reduced to brushing consistency with benzine or turpentine. It will dry in about twenty minutes, forming a hard, durable finish and may be obtained from a number of manufacturers.

CHAPTER XVII

CANE GLAZING

CANE for furniture comes in two forms, glazed or glossy and unglazed or dull and porous, of which the former is most generally encountered. The purpose is usually one of finishing to harmonize with the furniture color, walnut, mahogany or oak. This may be in a straight color or in a shaded, antique effect. On painted work the same or a shaded effect is customary.

Glazed.—The problem with glazed cane is primarily to make the color adhere, for the glossy surface holds out the finish and the uncertain anchorage afforded renders chipping and flaking easily accomplished. Three types of mixture are therefore used as follows:

(1) Dissolve in denatured alcohol equal parts Bismarck brown and spirit black and add an equal amount of white shellac. This will give a dark brown shade suitable for brown mahogany; the proportions of powder may be varied for a more reddish effect and for walnut, loutre brown may be substituted for Bismarck brown. In fact any combination of spirit soluble anilines may be employed to secure the desired shade. If it is desired to high-light, this should be done with a spray.

(2) In a similar way dry colors, such as siennas and umbers, rose pink and Van Dyke brown, may be mixed in turpentine and japan dryer with a little linseed oil added to make it possible to high-light by wiping. Japan colors may also be employed, reducing with turpentine and adding a little boiled oil. These mixtures should be applied thin and may be brushed or sprayed on.

(3) On cheaper work penetrating oil stains may be applied, slightly reduced with benzole to increase penetration, and with

212

a small amount of japan dryer added to hasten the drying.

Unglazed.—Unglazed cane readily absorbs the color and is most easily finished with one or another of the spirit shellac or lacquer shading mixtures described in Book I, Chapter I. Mixtures containing oil are best not used as they may tend to darken the cane excessively. Solid woven cane is of a coarser weave and is used chiefly on porch and utility chairs, being finished with the same varnish as the frame.

Protecting.—To protect the color glazes mentioned, a coat of clear flat lacquer is suitable for all but (3) ; flat varnish may be, and customarily is, used on all. There is no objection to a gloss lacquer or varnish providing this lustre is satisfactory.

CHAPTER XVIII

PIANO FINISHING METHODS

WHEN the piano comes from the cabinet shop, sponge the case with hot water. Let the case dry and sand down with 2/0 garnet finishing paper, using a cork block over the paper. By this method the grain of the wood is raised and sanded off before using water stain, otherwise the water stain will raise the grain too much for a good finishing surface.

Staining.—Prepare water red and brown in desired proportions for walnut and mahogany cases, or for golden oak, prepare brown alone. Two parts of red and one part of brown will make a fiery red mahogany stain. One part of red and two parts of brown will make a good Colonial mahogany stain. These proportions may be varied as desired, and nigrosine (black) crystals can be added if a darker shade is desired for any formula. These stains must be prepared in hot water, as outlined in Chapter IV, Book II, except one-fourth pint of corn syrup is added to the stain while hot and thoroughly mixed. Apply this stain while hot with a three-inch brush, being careful to cover the surface thoroughly. Brush out the stain with the grain of the wood and with a stroke the full length of the piece on which you are working. The stain may be wiped to insure a good even coverage, using cloths that will not allow lint to catch in the grain. Allow at least ten hours for drying.

Wash Coat of Shellac.—A much better finish is obtained if the stain is covered with a wash coat of shellac and then sanded to cut off the little fibres that are raised by the staining. Prepare one to two inches of four-pound cut shellac in the bottom of a gallon pail and then fill up with alcohol; mix thoroughly and apply quickly and evenly without brushing out. As soon

214

as this coat is dry, which will take four or five hours, sand the surface lightly with 5/0 garnet finishing paper, being careful not to disturb the stain coat. Clean up for filler coat.

Filler.—Use a selected filler of a color to match the stain and apply as usual across the grain, brushing in well. When the filler begins to dull, wipe off across the grain with tow, moss, wood wool, or burlap. Finally wipe lightly with the grain, being

Mahogany grand piano.

sure that every portion has been wiped clean, especially in the recesses and corners. The filler should dry in a heated room, at least eighteen hours before applying varnish.

First Coat.—The first coat of varnish should be thinned about one-tenth with spirits of turpentine and applied as usual, brushing thoroughly. Finish off each piece with the grain and avoid runs and sags. This coat should be allowed about one week for drying in a heated drying room. When sufficiently hard, sand lightly with 3/0 garnet finishing paper and wipe.

Second-Third-Fourth Coats.—The next three coats of varnish should be applied the same as the first, except that the varnish is not thinned, so as to get all the body necessary for good rubbing. Allow at least forty-eight hours for drying between these coats. Ample time for drying will prevent checking later on. Pianos finished by this method have been known to last ten years without checking.

Coarse Rubbing.—When the fourth coat is dry, usually in five to ten days (to permit as much shrinkage as possible to take place), rub with FF Italian pumice and water, using woven felt. Keep plenty of water on the surface and merely rub until a fairly level, smooth surface is obtained. Flush off with water and clean up with sponge and chamois.

Flow Coat.—There are special varnishes for the finish coat of a piano, known as "skin coats," and they do not need reducing, but if a heavy body varnish is used, it is necessary to reduce it about ten per cent with spirits of turpentine, as for the first coat. Flow this on heavily with little brushing in such a way that the varnish will flow out without brush marks. Pick out dirt specks.

TO PRODUCE A HIGH POLISH

After the flow coat has dried hard, it can be rubbed with FFF pumice stone and water. This coat should be rubbed to a very smooth surface. Wash off thoroughly and then rub with rottenstone and water, saving the spent rottenstone slush (sometimes known as "suds") in a glass covered with a cloth. This spent slush is used later on for hand-rubbing. The water is used in a pressed felt and rubbed over a brick rottenstone and then rubbed, with the grain, systematically over the surface until polished. Draw the palm over the surface at intervals to ascertain if sufficiently rubbed and ready for hand-polishing. A good practice is to rub with the grain for the pumice rubbing and across the grain for the rottenstone rubbing, thus eliminating the pumice scratches with the rottenstone, finally with the grain.

HAND POLISHING

Take two pieces of felt, cut 3x5, and one-fourth inch thick, place them together and soak with water and lay in a flat dish containing very little water. Rub rottenstone slush from the glass on the felt. Slap the hands on this felt hard and rub the surface across the grain until the scratches from the rottenstone disappear and then rub with the palm of the hands with the grain until a mirror-like finish is obtained. The hands must be quite damp at first, but almost dry for the finish rubbing. One must have hands free from callous spots to do good polishing and this can be obtained by rubbing the hands on a pumice stone brick with water. The piano is then oiled off with lemon oil polish and then spirited off with a rag dampened with alcohol and wrung out until it will not leave a freezing sensation to the face when applied. It is not safe to apply an alcohol rag to the finish, if this condition can be noticed. Of course it is understood that the oil is first wiped off with a rag, being careful that none of the rottenstone has been left in corners. After cleaning off, the alcohol rag sufficiently dry is used, and the surface is cleaned taking up the oil. It is frequently necessary to use a second alcohol rag in order to be sure all the oil has been removed.

SATIN FINISH

The flow coat is rubbed with FF pumice stone and water with a woven felt pad. This slush is then cleaned off and dried. Then flood the surface with a mixture of lemon oil polish and benzine and FFF pumice sifted on the surface with a sack or perforated shaker.

One must be careful to get the pumice stone evenly distributed over the surface and have enough oil on the surface to saturate the pumice. This mixture should form a slush on the surface. Wipe this slush off with the grain and continue to wipe dry

Liberal application of filler on mahogany piano.

afterward with clean cloths. This will produce a most beautiful satin finish.

Many machines have been designed for rubbing and can be used largely for coarse rubbing and even for fine rubbing where they are handled with accuracy.

Waterproof garnet paper, to some extent, has taken the place of pumice stone for fine rubbing, but piano factories are slow to change a system that has taken years to develop and perfect. Good work can be done with this paper, if properly handled, and it will cut faster than the pumice with a great deal less cleaning off after using.

Steelwool can also be used for fine sanding of piano surfaces.

ANTIQUE LACQUER FINISH

Water stain of desired shade is first applied, a typical one for *mahogany* consisting of 3 oz. bichromate of potash, 2 oz. jet nigrosene, ½ oz. mahogany brown, 2 oz. lemon yellow and 1 oz. walnut brown to 15 gallons water; for *walnut*, 1¼ oz. walnut brown and ¼ oz. mahogany brown to 2½ gallons water. This is followed by a wash coat of 2 parts 4-lb. cut white shellac to 1 part alcohol, and sanding, after which the method is the same for both woods.

The filler should be a black transparent one, reduced with naphtha to what would be a milk rather than the regular cream consistency as it is not intended to fill the pores flush. After wiping, the filler is allowed to dry 24 hours and is then shaded with the spirit shading stain formula described in Book I, Chapter IV. When dry, the case is finished with two coats medium lustre flat lacquer, applied at 24-hour intervals, the last coat rubbed with a waxed rag in 48 hours. All work is done by spraying.

BUILT UP LACQUER FINISH

Where a closer approximation of the conventional varnish system is desired, the following schedule is used. The work is stained and filled in the regular way, allowing 24 hours for the water stain to dry and 48 hours for the filler which is applied so as to fill the pores flush with the surface and using a filler constructed to withstand lacquer solvents. This is important. Now apply a coat of high-grade wood lacquer and allow a full 24 hours before applying the second coat. Allow 48 hours before applying the third coat, adding 24 hours to the drying of each successive lacquer coat; from four to seven coats may be applied, according to the depth and fullness of finish desired.

After the final coat of lacquer is on the work, it should be allowed to stand almost a week so that all lacquer solvents will evaporate and all of the shrinkage that is going to take place will have occurred before the lacquer surface is rubbed. After the surface has been rubbed it should be fine-rubbed and polished or fine-rubbed and left dull as desired, without applying further coats of lacquer. All work is done by spraying except filler.

CHAPTER XIX

IMITATION BURL WALNUT ON GUM WOOD

STAIN the wood with walnut crystals dissolved in hot water one shade lighter than the surrounding finish for a ground color Prepare three distemper colors of Van Dyke brown, burnt umber, and drop black, mixed with vinegar (white) to get the correct shade to match the walnut. This mixture should be the consistency of a heavy paste.

Dip a sponge in the vinegar and take enough color in the sponge to cover the surface with one stroke, lapping each stroke until the whole surface is covered evenly.

Prepare a woolen rag (preferably a piece of woolen pants) twenty inches long and from four to ten inches wide, depending on the width of the piece on which you are working. Fold this rag in pleats about one inch wide (the folds can be varied, depending on the size of the figure desired), and then soak it in water and squeeze out until the water will not run out of the rag when handling.

This folded rag must be rolled over the surface lightly and quickly before it is dry. The rag will pick up the color on the folded edges and leave the color between the folds, thus creating a good imitation of burl walnut finish. This of course must be blended out with a camelhair blender, four inches wide, with bristles at least three or four inches long. Blend lightly across the grain figure and then lightly with the grain. This whole operation must be performed with the finish wet.

Let dry about thirty minutes and apply brown colored lacquer or varnish, being careful not to disturb the distemper color, and to avoid this when using varnish, it must be applied quickly. The lacquer can be applied better with an air brush. After this coat is dry, sand lightly and finish with other coats as desired.

221

CHAPTER XX

BATIK ON WOOD, GESSO, GILDING, POLYCHROME

BATIK

S ELECT a design you wish to batik and then trace it on the piece you are decorating. This is best done by using a pouncing pad, but if one is accomplished at drawing, the design may be traced on the wood with charcoal. The design is then covered with paraffine wax used in a tool known as the Reinann batik pencil. Other tools may be used, but this one produces the best results.

Use an alcohol lamp to heat the wax, as the wax must always be fluid to flow easily, and apply the wax along the design you have drawn, filling in the part that you wish left in the natural wood. For larger surfaces a brush may be used for applying the wax.

The wax will prevent any stain penetrating this portion, and when the wax is removed, the design is left in the natural wood. Water stain is the best to use for staining the wood after the batik. Many colors of stain can be used by waxing all of the portion except the one you are staining each time you apply stain.

When the stain is dry, the wax is removed with a knife and the remaining wax rubbed into the wood with a woolen rag, thus finishing the wood with a semi-gloss polish.

GESSO

Gesso work is very fascinating and offers a wide field for design on wood, metal, paper, glass, etc. This work consists of building up a design in raised relief, so that the finish will

222

have the appearance of being carved. This material can be purchased at any art store. First draw your design on the wood, or trace it as you have been instructed above in batiking, and have a fine pencil brush for drawing your design. Always have a glass of water near by to keep your brush clean. In building up the design, keep your brush well filled with gesso and let it flow over the end of the brush. Use your fingers or a piece of wood or bent wire to keep the lines in perfect shape.

More coats of gesso can be applied to build up the design. Your taste alone is your limitation. The beauty of making designs of this kind is that if a mistake is made, the gesso can be removed and done over. After the design has been built up as desired, allow it to stand two hours for drying. You can then paint or stain the article any color you want, and after that you can paint, gild or color the gesso any desired shade, and in some instances the whole piece is sprayed with burnished gold and raised portions burnished with a burnishing tool.

GILDING

First give the article you wish gilded two coats of shellac. If you are working on metal, be sure that the metal is free from grease. To mix the gold size, thin the gilder's oil with turpentine to about the consistency of water, then mix a little chrome yellow and tint it with vermillion to give the gold size a gold color, running the size through a strainer, adding some varnish or a little japan drier, as experience may teach, so that the size will dry tacky. When applying the size, rub well into the crevices with a stiff bristle brush and let it stand for a minute or two so that the excess oil will run down. Then go over the whole surface with a soft piece of cheese cloth, saturated with gold size. Let it dry over night or about sixteen hours. For faster drying, mix accordingly more japan dryer.

Apply the gold leaf to the parts that are sized and have some cotton waste handy with which to rub the leaf down. With a clean piece of cheese cloth, rub the leaf until smooth. Be sure to rub some beeswax onto the cheese cloth so that the cloth will not scratch the gold leaf.

To get the gold leaf into the crevices, use an ordinary clothes brush, rub some wax on the brush, and in that way you save all of the waste leaf. After the gilding is done, go over the leaf with a thin coat of shellac so that the work will not tarnish and can be colored in antique as desired and explained under polychrome.

Schlagmetal may be used for cheaper work instead of genuine gold leaf.

POLYCHROME

Polychroming means a combination of colors, and any number of colors may be employed. In polychroming over metallic or bronzed surfaces, japan colors are used for quick drying. Any number of effects may be obtained by mixing metallic bronzes with colored enamels.

For instance, a lampshade is of black silk, gold and coral. You would wish the stand to carry out the same effect, so gold leaf the stand or bronze it, then trim it with coral and black.

In using japan colors, a thin coat of shellac is put on and then a glazed coat over the entire surface. This is done by mixing burnt umber ground in japan, with a small portion of burnt sienna thinned down with turpentine and wiped off as you see fit, using a piece of cheese cloth dampened in turpentine. Then with a soft brush or powder-puff, apply a coat of rotten stone which will adhere to the glazed coat. Then wipe off the extreme high lights. Another way to get an antique effect is to use burnt umber, mix it with turpentine, then stipple a thin coat of this on the work. Let this dry a few hours and use a piece of cheesecloth dampened in benzine, and wipe off in such a way as to obtain a scratchy effect. After this, brush on a thin coat of shellac or spray on a coat of lacquer. Follow this with a glazed coat of white lead, a little black and a little sienna, all ground in japan colors. Thin this down with benzine and brush it all over the surface and wipe off, leaving the glaze in the crevices.